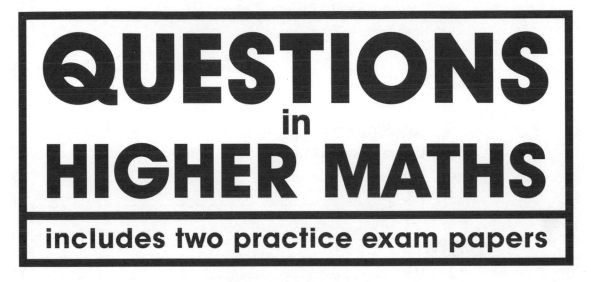

QUESTIONS in HIGHER MATHS

includes two practice exam papers

Ken Nisbet

2nd Edition

Published by
Leckie & Leckie Ltd
8 Whitehill Terrace
St Andrews Scotland KY16 8RN
tel: 01334 475656 fax: 01334 477392
hq@leckieandleckie.co.uk
www.leckieandleckie.co.uk

Special thanks to
Julie Barclay (design)
Tom Davie (production assistance)
Nicole Dewar (typing)
Emily Dewhurst (page make-up)
Catherine Gerrard (proofreading)
Bruce Ryan (project management)
Hamish Sanderson (illustration)

ISBN 1-898890-12-9

A CIP Catalogue record for this book is available from the British Library.

Printed in Scotland by Inglis Allen on environmentally friendly paper. The paper is made from a mixture of sawmill waste, forest thinnings and wood from sustainable forests.

® Leckie & Leckie is a registered trademark.

INVESTOR IN PEOPLE Leckie & Leckie Ltd achieved the Investors in People Standard in 1999.

Leckie & Leckie

with pull-out answer section

CONTENTS

What this book contains

There are three sections:

- **Skills and Techniques Revision**
  This is a bank of Exercises designed to give you extra practice with skills and techniques that frequently occur in exam questions.
- **Practice Exams**
  Two complete exams are provided. These are similar in range, structure and difficulty to the exam you will sit.
- **Answers and Solutions**
  This is a pull-out section containing the answers to the Exercises and also full solutions to the two Practice Exams. To pull out the answer section, remove the centre staple.

Leckie & Leckie's *Higher Maths Course Notes*

Questions in Higher Maths is the companion volume to Leckie & Leckie's *Higher Maths Course Notes*. We recommend that you work with both books when revising for your exam. Extensive references to the worked examples in the second edition of the *Course Notes* will be found beside most of the exercises in the *Questions* book.

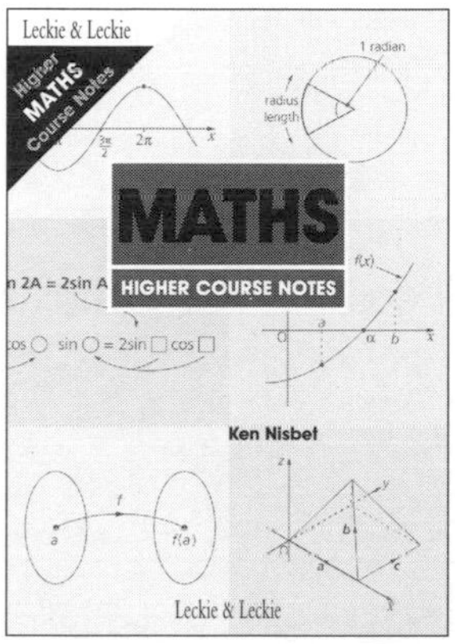

Suggestions for using this book

There are many ways of using the revision material in this book. You may decide to work through the exercises concentrating on the techniques and skills that you feel need the most practice. However we recommend that you attempt Practice Exam A as a timed exam. Write out your solutions with no help and stop when the allocated time is up. You can then compare your own solutions with the full solutions in the Answers Section. Identify weak areas and use the Skills and Techniques Exercises to practise these skills. When you have completed this task, wait a few days, and then resit the Exam Paper. Again identify continuing weaknesses and revisit the appropriate Exercises. This same approach should then be repeated using Practice Exam B. It is this repetitive practice of problems that will improve your chances of achieving a good grade in the final examination.

Additional Comments

There is a deliberate mixing of questions of C level and A/B level difficulty in the Exercises section and no attempt has been made to identify these different levels. This is because we strongly believe that what may be considered as A/B level difficulty skills are as achievable as those considered to be at C level difficulty provided enough practice and effort is devoted to their mastery.

It is not possible in a book of this nature to cover all the material that is likely to occur in your exam and it is therefore vital that you attempt as many of the actual Past Papers as you can. We hope that this book, along with the *Higher Maths Course Notes*, helps you towards achieving a good grade in your final examination.

Additional Comments (cont.)

The following formulae are made available to you during your exam:

The equation $x^2 + y^2 + 2gx + 2fy + c = 0$ represents a circle centre $(-g, -f)$ and radius $\sqrt{(g^2 + f^2 - c)}$

The equation $(x - a)^2 + (y - b)^2 = r^2$ represents a circle centre (a, b) and radius r.

Scalar Product: $\mathbf{a}.\mathbf{b} = |\mathbf{a}|\,|\mathbf{b}| \cos\theta$, where θ is the angle between **a** and **b**

or

$$\mathbf{a}.\mathbf{b} = a_1b_1 + a_2b_2 + a_3b_3 \text{ where } \mathbf{a} = \begin{pmatrix} a_1 \\ a_2 \\ a_3 \end{pmatrix} \text{ and } \mathbf{b} = \begin{pmatrix} b_1 \\ b_2 \\ b_3 \end{pmatrix}$$

Trigonometric formulae:

$\sin(A \pm B) = \sin A \cos B \pm \cos A \sin B$

$\cos(A \pm B) = \cos A \cos B \mp \sin A \sin B$

$$\begin{aligned} \cos 2A &= \cos^2 A - \sin^2 A \\ &= 2\cos^2 A - 1 \\ &= 1 - 2\sin^2 A \end{aligned}$$

$\sin 2A = 2\sin A \cos A$

Table of standard derivatives:

$f(x)$	$f'(x)$
$\sin ax$	$a\cos ax$
$\cos ax$	$-a\sin ax$

Table of standard integrals:

$f(x)$	$\int f(x)\,dx$
$\sin ax$	$-\frac{1}{a}\cos ax + C$
$\cos ax$	$\frac{1}{a}\sin ax + C$

SKILLS AND TECHNIQUES REVISION

See these pages in Leckie & Leckie's *Higher Maths Course Notes:*

Exercise 1.1 The Gradient Formula

page 3, example 1.2

Find the gradient of the line joining the given pairs of points:

1. A(3, 5), B(5, 7) **2.** P(1, –1), Q(3, 5) **3.** R(1, 1), S(3, –5)

4. M(–3, –5), N(5, –1) **5.** O(0, 0), T(–1, 5) **6.** C(–7, –1), D(3, –6)

7. V(7, –2), W(12, –2) **8.** G(1, $-\frac{3}{2}$), H(3,–1)

Exercise 1.2 Angles and the x-axis

page 4, example 1.3

Find the angle that each line in Exercise 1.1 above makes with the positive direction of the x-axis.

Exercise 1.3 Collinear points – using gradients

1. In each case decide whether P lies on the line passing through A and B:

a. A(–2, 1), B(1, 4); P(4, 8) **b.** A(–2, 4), B(–1, 2); P(1, –2)

c. A(5, 1), B(–1, –2); P(–3, –3) **d.** A(2, –4), B(0, 2); P(–2, 6)

e. A($\frac{5}{2}$, 0), B($\frac{1}{2}$, 1); P($-\frac{3}{2}$, 2)

Hint: Find m_{AB} and m_{BP}

2. A Radar Operator notices an aircraft at T(2, –1). After a few minutes she observes it at U(–1, 2). There are airports at A_1(–8, 8) and A_2(–8, 9). For which airport is it heading if it does not change course?

Exercise 1.4 Perpendicular lines

page 4, example 1.5

1. Show that each triangle ABC is right-angled at B:

a.

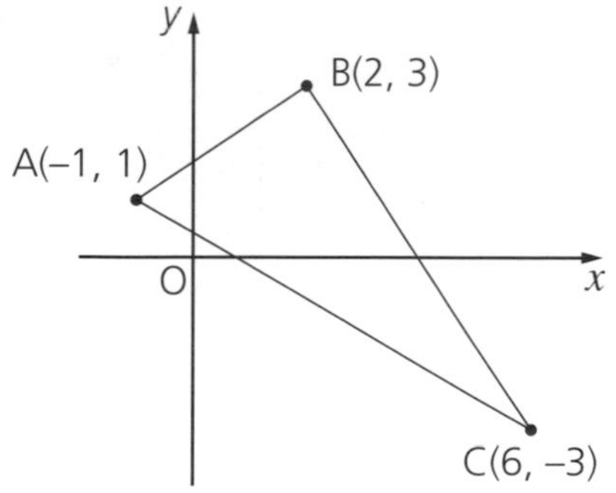

b.

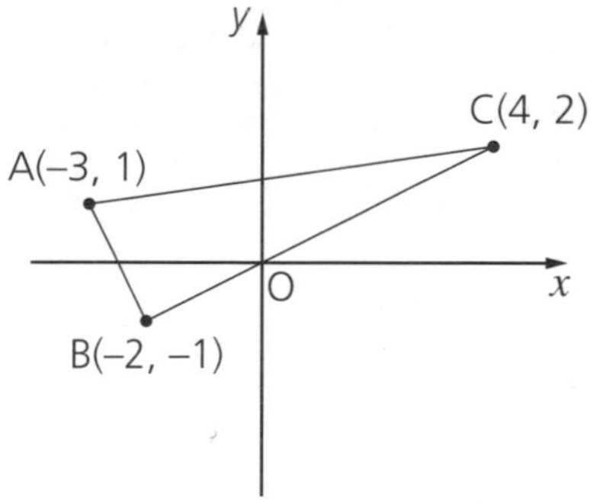

2. Show that each set of three points forms a right-angled triangle and name the right-angle in each case:

a. P(–8, 3), Q(–3, 4), R(–6, –7) **b.** C(–8, –7), D(8, 4), E(–2, 8)

c. U(–7, 0), V(–5, –7), W(7, 4) **d.** A(–5, –1), B(–9, –3), C(–2, –7)

Exercise 1.5 Perpendicular gradients

See these pages in Leckie & Leckie's *Higher Maths Course Notes:*

page 4, example 1.6

1. Find the gradient of lines perpendicular to AB where:

a. $m_{AB} = \frac{3}{4}$ **b.** $m_{AB} = -\frac{2}{3}$ **c.** $m_{AB} = 5$

d. $m_{AB} = -2$ **e.** $m_{AB} = 0$ **f.** $m_{AB} = \frac{1}{3}$

g. $m_{AB} = -\frac{1}{2}$ **h.** $m_{AB} = -\frac{5}{2}$ **i.** $m_{AB} = 1{\cdot}5$

2. Find the gradient of lines perpendicular to AB where:

a. A(2, 3), B(4, 6) **b.** A(–1, 3), B(1, 8)

c. A(4, 2), B(6, 1) **d.** A(–3, 4), B(–1, 1)

Exercise 1.6 Points on lines

Decide in each case whether the point lies on the line:

1. (2, 3); $3x + 2y = 12$ **2.** (–2, 1); $3x - 2y = -4$ **3.** (–2, –3); $x - 3y = 7$

4. $(\frac{1}{2}, 1)$; $-2x + y = -1$ **5.** $(-1, \frac{1}{2})$; $3x = 2y - 4$ **6.** $(-\frac{1}{2}, \frac{3}{2})$; $x + 2 = y$

Hint: Substitute the x- and y-coordinate values into the equation.

Exercise 1.7 Equation of a line from point and gradient

page 6, example 1.9

Find the equation of the line passing through the given point with the given gradient:

1. (2, 3); 2 **2.** (1, –3); $\frac{1}{2}$ **3.** (–2, 5); $-\frac{1}{2}$

4. (5, –1); –3 **5.** (0, 4); –1 **6.** $(\frac{3}{2}, 0)$; $\frac{1}{2}$

Exercise 1.8 Axes intercepts

page 6, example 1.11

For each line find the points of intersection with the x- and y-axes.

1. $y = 3x + 6$ **2.** $2y - 3x = 6$ **3.** $3y + x = 6$

4. $2y - 5x - 10 = 0$ **5.** $5y - 2x = 5$ **6.** $3y + 2x + 5 = 0$

Exercise 1.9 Simultaneous equations

page 6, example 1.12

1. For each pair of lines find their point of intersection:

a. $2x - y = -1$, $x + 2y = 12$ **b.** $x + 3y - 8 = 0$, $3x + 2y - 3 = 0$ **c.** $4x + 3y - 10 = 0$, $2x - y - 10 = 0$

d. $6x - y - 3 = 0$, $2x + 3y - 1 = 0$ **e.** $5x = 2y - 2$, $2x = 3y + 8$ **f.** $2x + 4y + 5 = 0$, $y = -3x$

2. Determine whether or not these lines are concurrent:

a. $2x + y - 7 = 0$, $x + 2y - 11 = 0$ and $3x - y + 2 = 0$

b. $3x - y + 2 = 0$, $2x + 3y + 5 = 0$ and $x - y + 1 = 0$

c. $x + y - 1 = 0$, $5x + 2y + 4 = 0$ and $3x - y + 8 = 0$

d. $2x - y = 0$, $6x + 5y = 8$ and $4x - 3y + 1 = 0$

Hint: Solve only one pair simultaneously then use the method from Exercise 1.6 above for the third line.

Exercise 1.10 The Distance Formula

Find the distance between these points:

1. (2, 1), (5, 5) **2.** (–5, 1), (1, 9) **3.** (5, –1), (1, –4)

4. (10, 0), (–2, –5) **5.** $(\frac{1}{2}, -1), (-\frac{1}{2}, 0)$ **6.** $(\frac{3}{2}, -2), (-\frac{1}{2}, -6)$

7. (0, 0), (–2, 8) **8.** $(-\frac{3}{2}, \frac{3}{2}), (-2, 1)$

Exercise 1.11 The Midpoint Formula

Find the coordinates of M, the midpoint of the line joining the given pair of points.

1. (2, 3), (10, 1) **2.** (–2, 3), (4, 5) **3.** (–3, 1), (–1, –3)

4. (–10, –1), (–2, –3) **5.** (1, 5), (4, –2) **6.** $(\frac{1}{2}, -\frac{3}{2}), (\frac{3}{2}, -\frac{1}{2})$

7. (0, 0), (–2, 7) **8.** $(-\frac{3}{2}, 0), (\frac{1}{2}, -3)$

Exercise 1.12 Perpendicular bisectors

Find the equation of the perpendicular bisector of the line joining:

1. A(–1, 1), B(3, 7) **2.** P(0, 4), Q(2, 2) **3.** R(–1, –1), S(3, 1)

4. T(–8, 6), U(–2, 4) **5.** C(–1, –2), D(3, 0) **6.** E(0, 2), F(–2, 8)

7. J(–2, –1), K(–4, 0) **8.** L(–3, –1), M(–7, 0)

Hint: First use Exercise 1.1, then Exercise 1.5, then Exercise 1.11, then Exercise 1.7.

Exercise 1.13 Equation of median and point of intersection

1. For each triangle find the equations of the two indicated medians and hence find G, their point of intersection.

a.

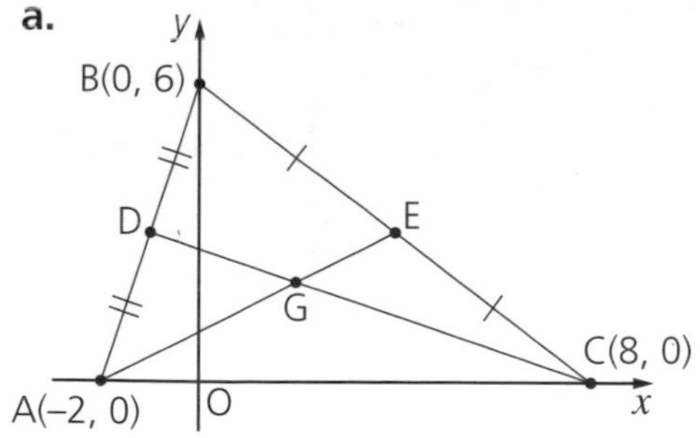

b.

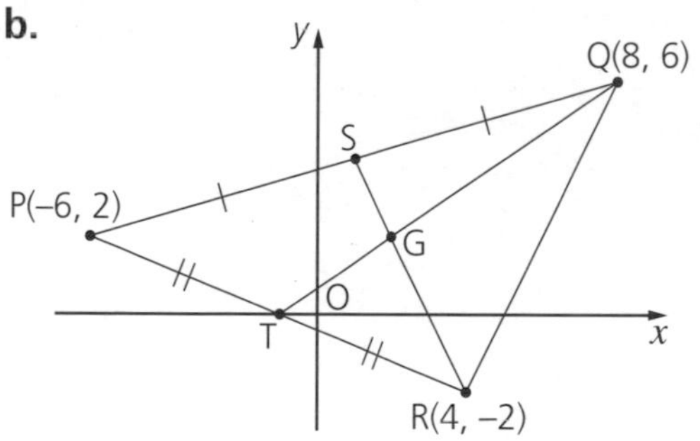

2.

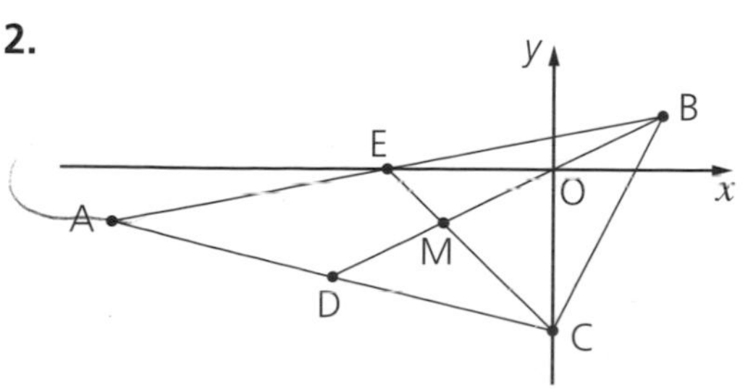

A triangle has vertices A(–8, –1), B(2, 1) and C(0, –3). The medians BD and CE intersect at M.

a. Find the equations of BD and CE.

b. Hence find the coordinates of M.

(This Exercise combines the skills of Exercises 1.1, 1.7, 1.9 and 1.11.)

See these pages in Leckie & Leckie's *Higher Maths Course Notes:*

page 7
Use of the formula is illustrated in example 1.13.

page 7, example 1.14

3.

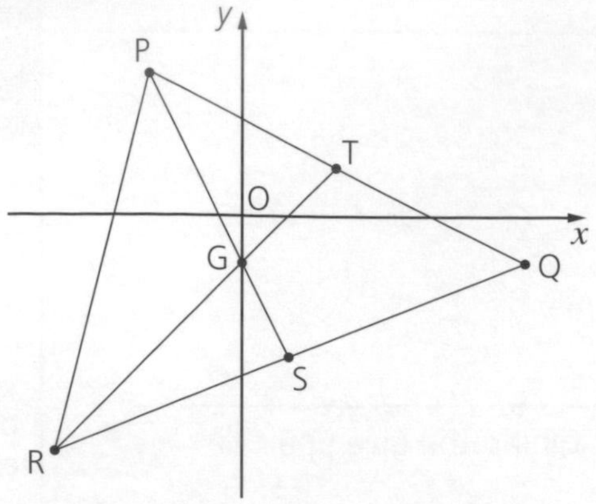

A triangle has vertices P(–2, 3), Q(6, –1) and R(–4, –5). Find the coordinates of G, the point of intersection of the medians PS and RT.

4. For triangle ABC where A(–5, 1), B(7, 5) and C(7, –9), show that the three medians are concurrent.

Hint: Use the method from Exercise 1.6 for the third median.

See these pages in Leckie & Leckie's *Higher Maths Course Notes:*

2. NUMBERS, SETS AND NOTATION

This topic involves only notation. There are no skills and techniques to practise.

See these pages in Leckie & Leckie's *Higher Maths Course Notes:*

page 8.
Learn the notation.

Exercise 3.1 Suitable domains

See these pages in Leckie & Leckie's *Higher Maths Course Notes:*

page 9, example 3.1

State a suitable domain for the function f.

1. $f(x) = \frac{1}{x}$ **2.** $f(x) = \frac{x+1}{x+2}$ **3.** $f(x) = \frac{x}{x-4}$

4. $f(x) = \frac{3}{x^2-1}$ **5.** $f(x) = \frac{x+2}{x^2-4}$ **6.** $f(x) = \frac{3x+2}{x^2-16}$

7. $f(x) = \frac{2x-1}{3x^2}$ **8.** $f(x) = \frac{x-5}{9-4x^2}$ **9.** $f(x) = \sqrt{x-4}$

10. $f(x) = \sqrt{x+3}$ **11.** $f(x) = \sqrt{10-x}$ **12.** $f(x) = \sqrt{5-2x}$

Exercise 3.2 Points on graphs

In each case the given point lies on the graph $y = f(x)$. Find the value of b.

1. $(3, b)$, $f(x) = 2x + 3$ **2.** $(1, b)$, $f(x) = x^2 - 3$

3. $(-2, b)$, $f(x) = 3x^3 - x^2$ **4.** $(\frac{1}{2}, b)$, $f(x) = 1 - 2x - x^2$

5. $(-1, b)$, $f(x) = 2x^4 + 2x^2$ **6.** $(-4, b)$, $f(x) = x^2 - x - 1$

Hint: Substitute the x-coordinate value into the formula to obtain b.

Exercise 3.3 Graphs of related functions

page 9.
The diagram at the bottom of the page should help.

The graph of $y = f(x)$ is shown. Sketch the indicated graphs showing clearly the images of the named points.

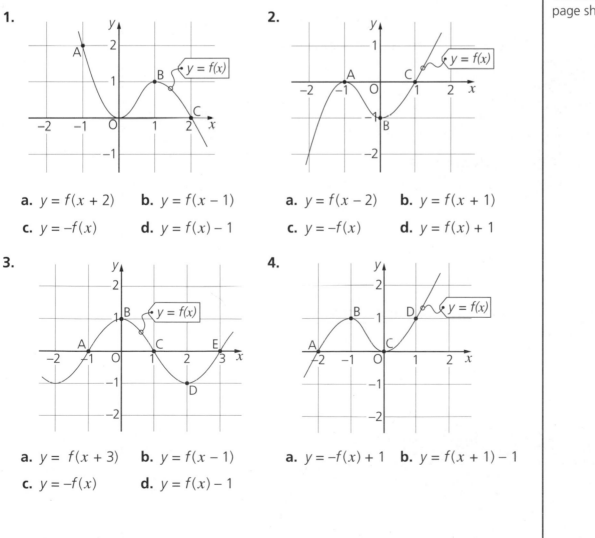

1.

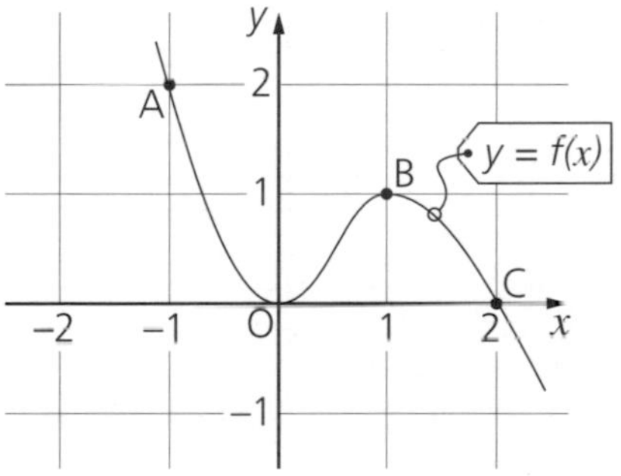

a. $y = f(x + 2)$ **b.** $y = f(x - 1)$

c. $y = -f(x)$ **d.** $y = f(x) - 1$

2.

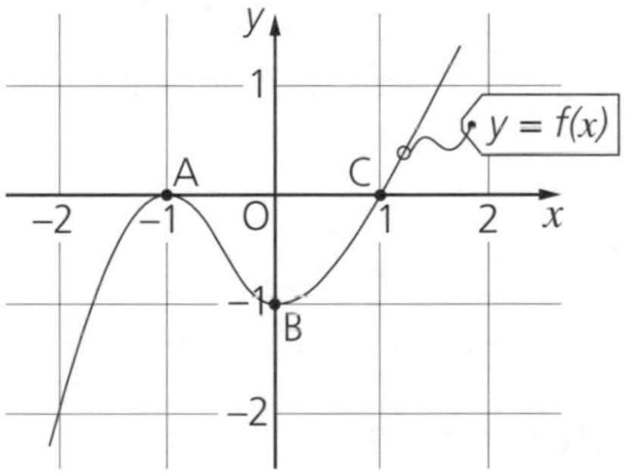

a. $y = f(x - 2)$ **b.** $y = f(x + 1)$

c. $y = -f(x)$ **d.** $y = f(x) + 1$

3.

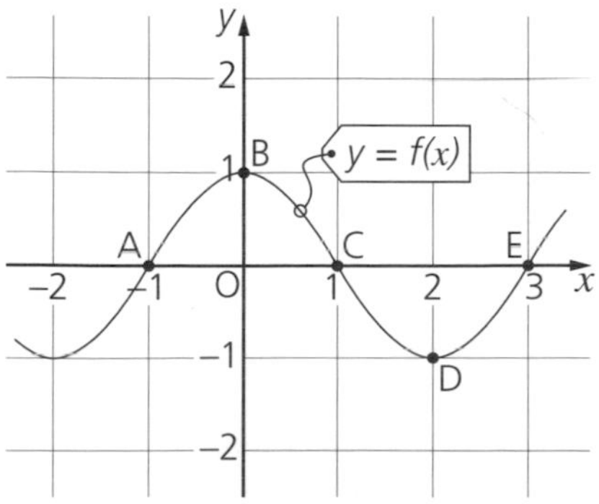

a. $y = f(x + 3)$ **b.** $y = f(x - 1)$

c. $y = -f(x)$ **d.** $y = f(x) - 1$

4.

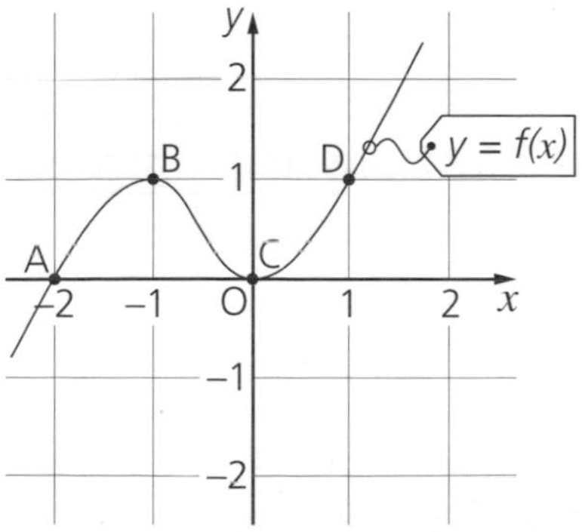

a. $y = -f(x) + 1$ **b.** $y = f(x + 1) - 1$

See these pages in Leckie & Leckie's *Higher Maths Course Notes:*

page 10, example 3.2

5.

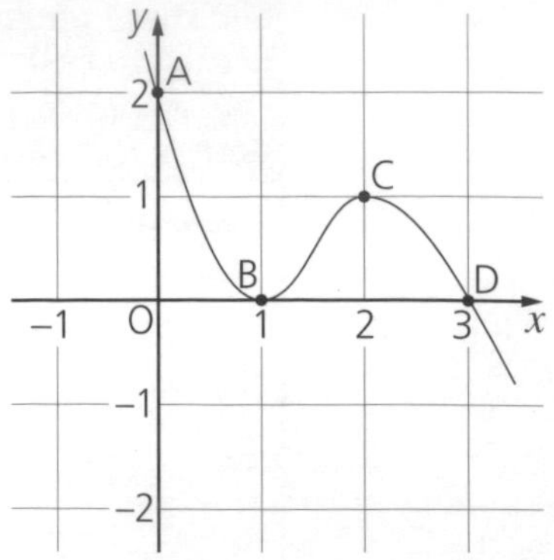

6.

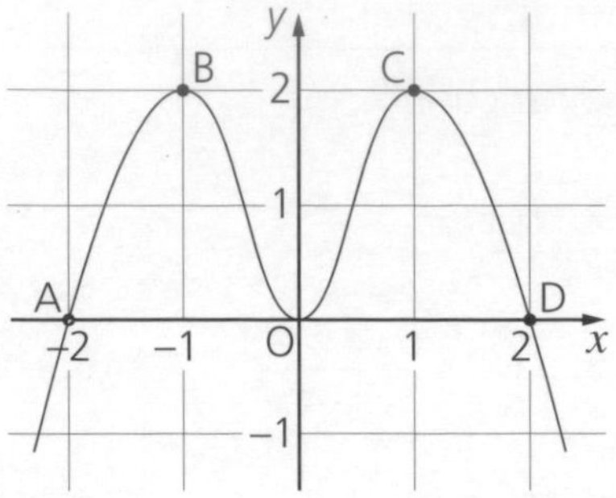

5. **a.** $y = -f(x) + 2$ **b.** $y = f(x + 1) - 1$

6. **a.** $y = 1 - f(x)$ **b.** $y = -f(x + 2)$

Exercise 3.4 Composite functions

page 10 example 3.4

1. $f(x) = 4x - 1$, find:

a. $f(x^2)$ **b.** $f(2x)$ **c.** $f(x + 1)$ **d.** $f(3 - x)$

2. $g(x) = x^2 + 2$, find:

a. $g(2x)$ **b.** $g(x - 1)$ **c.** $g(3x + 1)$ **d.** $g(2 - 5x)$

3. $f(x) = 3x - 1$ and $g(x) = x^2$, find:

a. $g(f(x))$ **b.** $f(g(x))$ **c.** $f(f(x))$ **d.** $g(g(x))$

4. Find **(i)** $g(f(x))$ and **(ii)** $f(g(x))$ when:

a. $f(x) = 3x$ and $g(x) = 2x + 1$ **b.** $f(x) = x^2$ and $g(x) = 2x$

c. $f(x) = x - 5$ and $g(x) = x^2$ **d.** $f(x) = 1 + 2x$ and $g(x) = x^2 - 2$

5. $f(x) = 2 - x$ and $g(x) = 2x + k$

a. Find $f(g(x))$

b. Find $g(f(x))$

c. Show that $f(g(x)) + g(f(x)) = 6 - 4x$

d. Find $g(f(x)) - f(g(x))$

6. $f(x) = 2x$ and $g(x) = x^2 - m$

a. Show that $g(f(x)) - f(g(x)) = 2x^2 + m$

b. Show that $(f(x))^2 - g(f(x)) = m$

Exercise 3.5 Composite functions and algebraic fractions

1. Simplify by writing as a single fraction:

a. $2 \times \frac{1}{x} - 1$ **b.** $1 - 4 \times \frac{1}{x}$ **c.** $2 \times \frac{1}{x-1} + 1$

d. $2 \times \frac{1}{x-1} - 1$ **e.** $1 + 4 \times \frac{1}{x+1}$ **f.** $1 - 3 \times \frac{1}{x-1}$

g. $4 \times \frac{1}{x^2-9} + 1$ **h.** $3 \times \frac{1}{x^2-1} - 1$

Hint: $1 - 5 \times \frac{1}{x+2} = \frac{x+2}{x+2} - \frac{5}{x+2} = \frac{x+2-5}{x+2} = \frac{x-3}{x+2}$

See these pages in Leckie & Leckie's *Higher Maths Course Notes:*

2. For the functions f and g, defined on suitable domains, find an expression for $h(x)$ where $h(x) = g(f(x))$. Give your answer as a single fraction.

a. $f(x) = \frac{1}{x}$ and $g(x) = 2x - 1$ **b.** $f(x) = \frac{1}{x+1}$ and $g(x) = 3x + 1$

c. $f(x) = \frac{1}{x-1}$ and $g(x) = 1 - 2x$ **d.** $f(x) = \frac{1}{x^2-1}$ and $g(x) = 2x + 1$

e. $f(x) = \frac{1}{x^2-9}$ and $g(x) = 3x - 1$ **f.** $f(x) = \frac{1}{x^2-1}$ and $g(x) = 1 + 2x$

Exercise 3.6 Exponential and logarithmic graphs

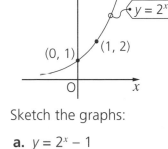

page 13, example 3.6

1.

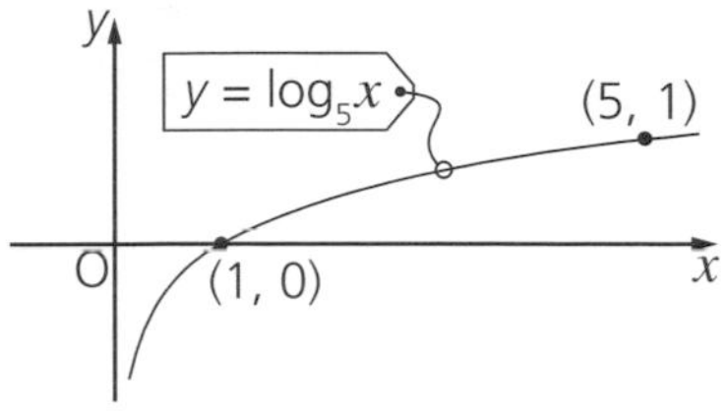

Sketch the graphs:

a. $y = \log_5 x + 1$

b. $y = \log_5(x + 1)$

c. $y = -\log_5 x$

d. $y = \log_5(x - 2) - 1$

2.

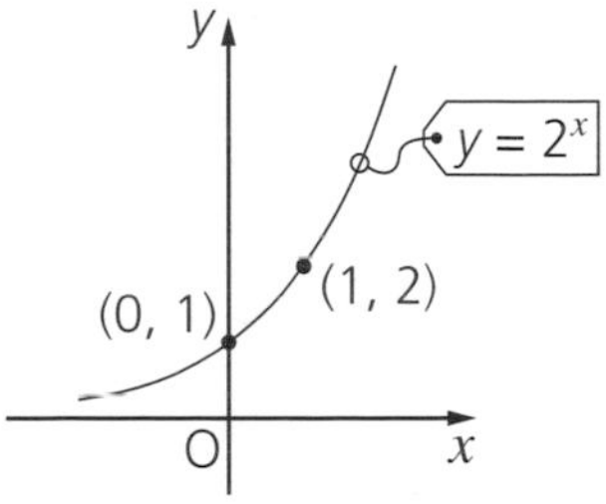

Sketch the graphs:

a. $y = 2^x - 1$

b. $y = 2^{x+1}$

c. $y = 2^{x-1}$

d. $y = -2^x$

Exercise 3.7 Completing the square

page 13, example 3.7

1. Express $f(x)$ in the form $(x + b)^2 + c$:

a. $x^2 + 4x + 3$ **b.** $x^2 - 6x - 1$ **c.** $x^2 + 3x + 1$

d. $x^2 + 5x + 2$ **e.** $x^2 - 5x + 2$ **f.** $x^2 - x - 4$

g. $x^2 + x - 7$ **h.** $x^2 + 5x$

2. Express $f(x)$ in the form $a(x^2 + bx + c)$:

a. $2x^2 - 4x + 1$ **b.** $3x^2 + 6x + 2$ **c.** $5x^2 + 15x - 7$

d. $2x^2 - 10x - 5$ **e.** $4x^2 + 12x + 17$ **f.** $7x^2 - 28x - 12$

g. $2x^2 + 3x - 1$ **h.** $3x^2 + 5x + 7$

3. Express $f(x)$ in the form $a(x + b)^2 + c$:

a. $f(x) = 2x^2 + 4x + 1$ **b.** $f(x) = 3x^2 - 6x - 2$

c. $f(x) = (2x + 3)(2x + 5)$ **d.** $f(x) = (2x - 1)(2x - 3)$

e. $f(x) = (3x + 2)(3x + 4)$ **f.** $f(x) = (5x - 1)(5x + 11)$

g. $f(x) = (2x - 1)(x + 2)$ **h.** $f(x) = 6(x + 1) + (5x - 1)(x - 2)$

4. TRIGONOMETRY – BASIC FACTS

Exercise 4.1 Using the Sine and Cosine Graph

See these pages in Leckie & Leckie's Higher Maths Course Notes:

These graphs appear on page 15.

Solve:

1. $\sin x^\circ = 0$ for $0 \le x \le 360$
2. $\cos x^\circ = 1$ for $0 \le x < 360$
3. $\cos x^\circ = -1$ for $0 \le x \le 360$
4. $\sin x^\circ = 1$ for $0 \le x < 360$
5. $\cos x^\circ = 1$ for $0 \le x \le 360$
6. $\sin x^\circ = -1$ for $0 \le x < 360$
7. $\cos x^\circ = 0$ for $180 \le x \le 360$
8. $\sin x^\circ = 0$ for $180 < x \le 360$

Hint: Read the inequality for x carefully.

Exercise 4.2 Exact Values

page 15, example 4.1

1. Find the exact value of:

a. $\sin 45^\circ$ **b.** $\sin \frac{\pi}{3}$ **c.** $\cos 60^\circ$

d. $\cos 45^\circ$ **e.** $\tan \frac{\pi}{4}$ **f.** $\tan 60^\circ$

g. $\cos \frac{\pi}{6}$ **h.** $\sin \frac{\pi}{6}$ **i.** $\tan 45^\circ$

j. $\sin \frac{\pi}{4}$ **k.** $\cos 30^\circ$ **l.** $\tan \frac{\pi}{6}$

2. Find the value of x, where $0 \le x \le 90$ or $0 \le x \le \frac{\pi}{2}$ (i.e. 1st quadrant angle only). Take care... some are in degrees and some are in radians.

a. $\sin x^\circ = \frac{\sqrt{3}}{2}$ **b.** $\tan x = \sqrt{3}$ **c.** $\cos x = \frac{1}{2}$

d. $\cos x^\circ = \frac{\sqrt{3}}{2}$ **e.** $\tan x^\circ = \frac{1}{\sqrt{3}}$ **f.** $\cos x^\circ = \frac{1}{\sqrt{2}}$

g. $2\sin x - \sqrt{3} = 0$ **h.** $\sqrt{3}\tan x - 1 = 0$

Exercise 4.3 Max/Min Stationary Points on Trig Graphs

The graphs on page 16 should help you to find the coordinates. (1st ed: page 34)

1. Give the coordinates of the maximum and minimum stationary points on these graphs for $0 \le x \le 2\pi$.

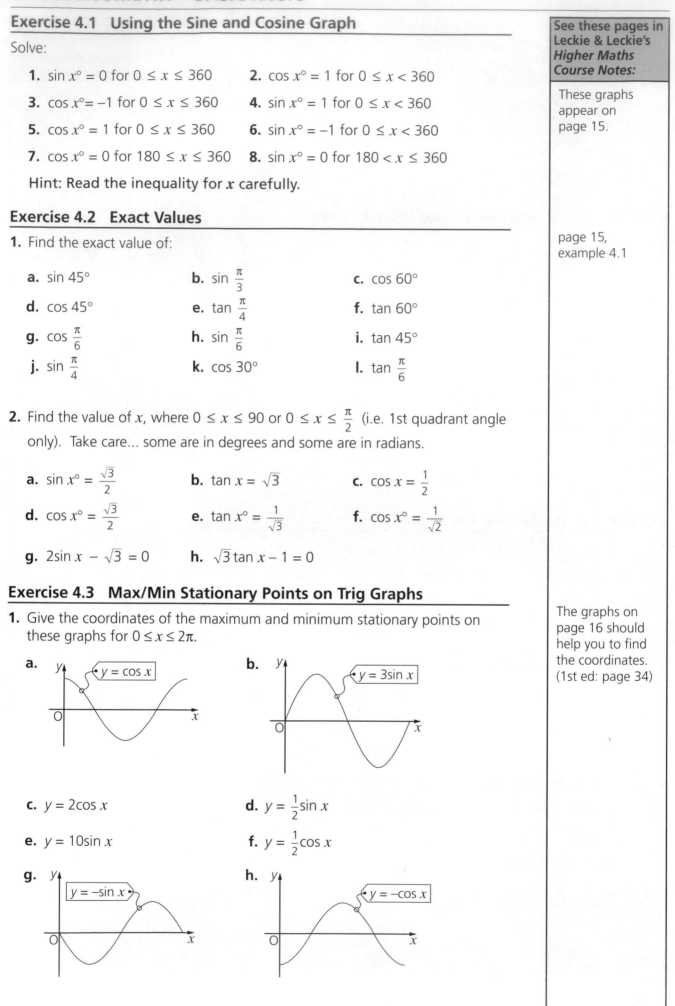

a.

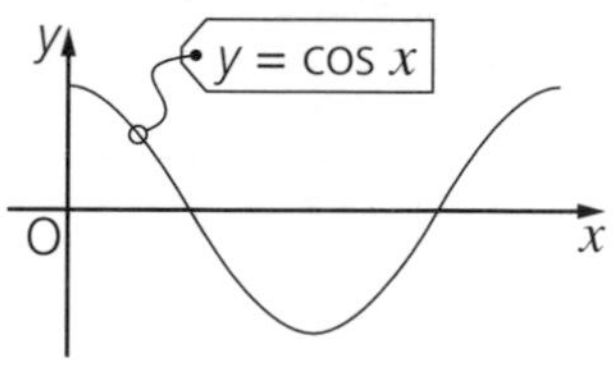

b.

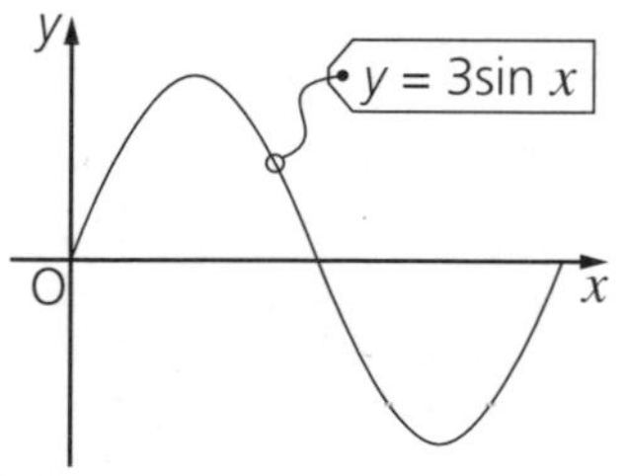

c. $y = 2\cos x$ **d.** $y = \frac{1}{2}\sin x$

e. $y = 10\sin x$ **f.** $y = \frac{1}{2}\cos x$

g.

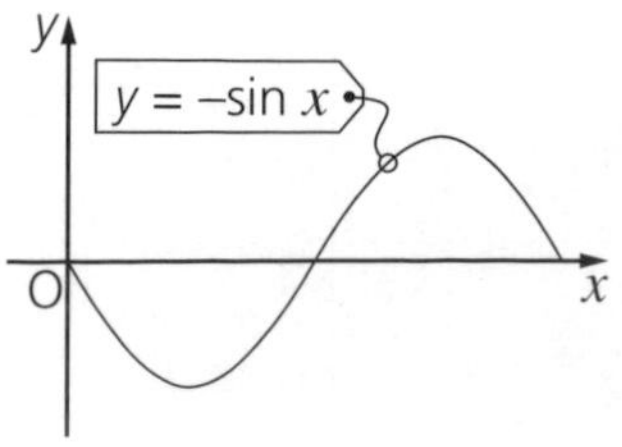

h.

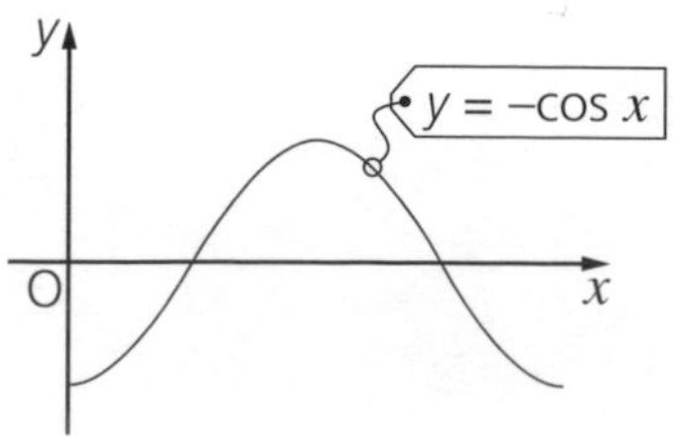

See these pages in Leckie & Leckie's *Higher Maths Course Notes:*

2. Simplify the following radian expressions:

a. $\frac{\pi}{2} - \frac{\pi}{3}$ **b.** $\frac{3\pi}{2} + \frac{\pi}{6}$ **c.** $\frac{3\pi}{2} + \frac{\pi}{4}$

d. $\frac{\pi}{2} - \frac{\pi}{6}$ **e.** $\frac{3\pi}{2} - \frac{\pi}{3}$ **f.** $\frac{\pi}{2} + \frac{\pi}{4}$

g. $\frac{\pi}{2} + \frac{\pi}{6}$ **h.** $2\pi - \frac{\pi}{6}$ **i.** $\pi + \frac{\pi}{3}$

3. Find the coordinates of the maximum and minimum stationary points on each graph for $0 \le x \le 2\pi$.

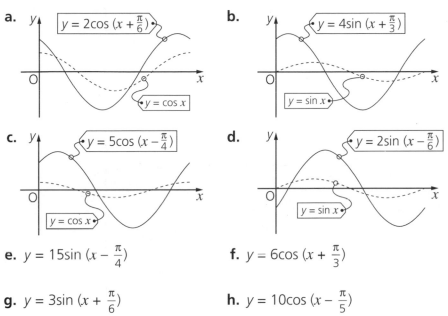

page 17, example 4.2 (1st ed: page 35, example 10.1)

a.

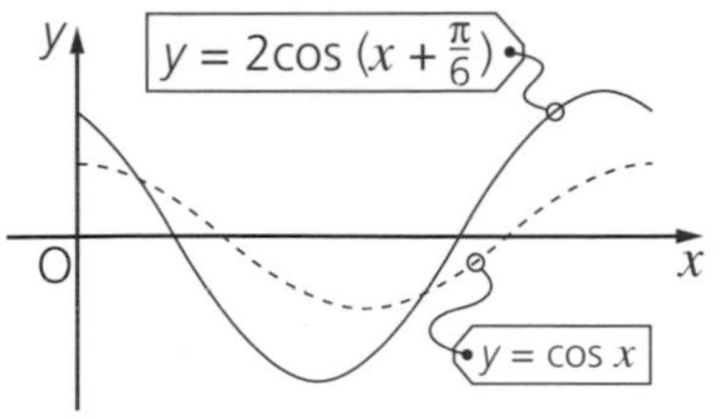

b.

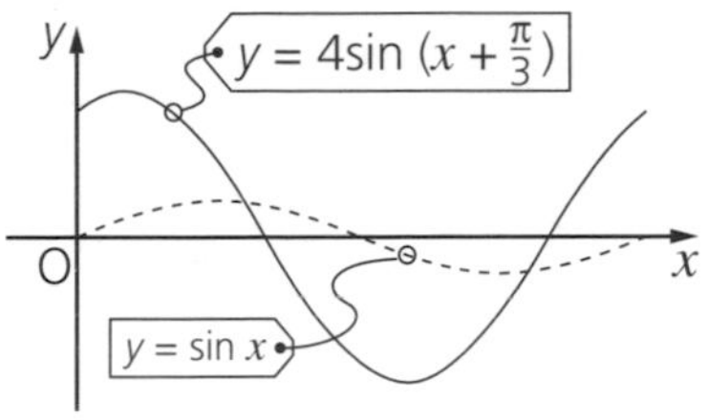

c.

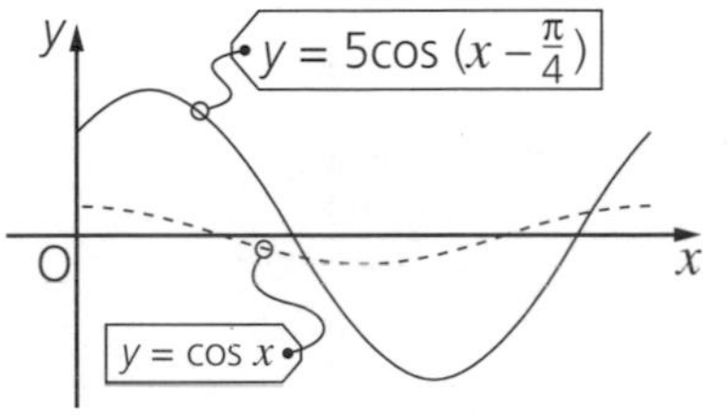

d.

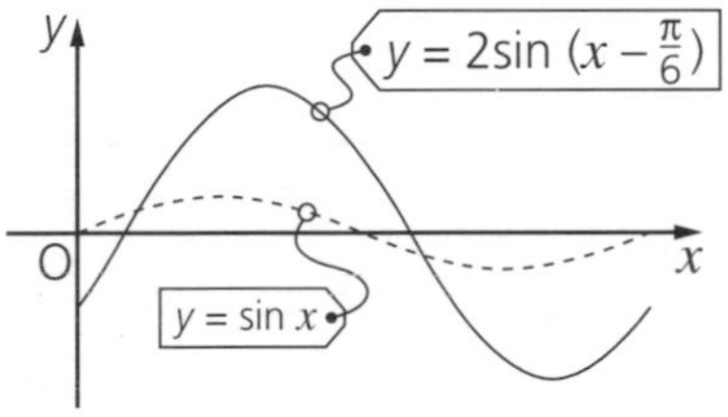

e. $y = 15\sin\left(x - \frac{\pi}{4}\right)$ **f.** $y = 6\cos\left(x + \frac{\pi}{3}\right)$

g. $y = 3\sin\left(x + \frac{\pi}{6}\right)$ **h.** $y = 10\cos\left(x - \frac{\pi}{5}\right)$

Exercise 4.4 Formulae of Related Graphs

page 17, example 4.3 (1st ed: page 35, example 10.2)

1. Find the value of *a* for each graph:

a.

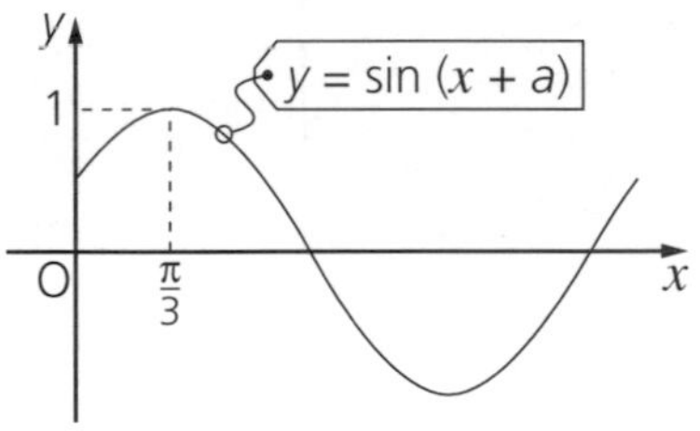

b.

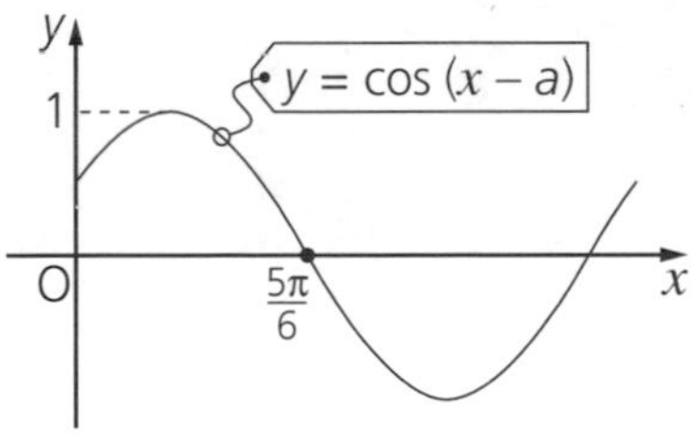

2. Find the values of *a* and *b* for each graph:

a.

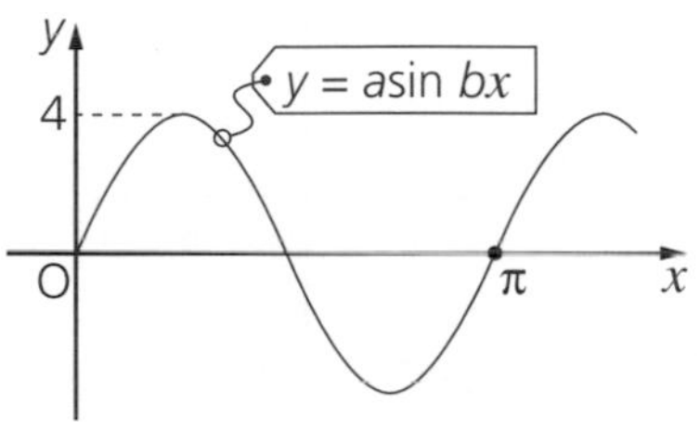

b.

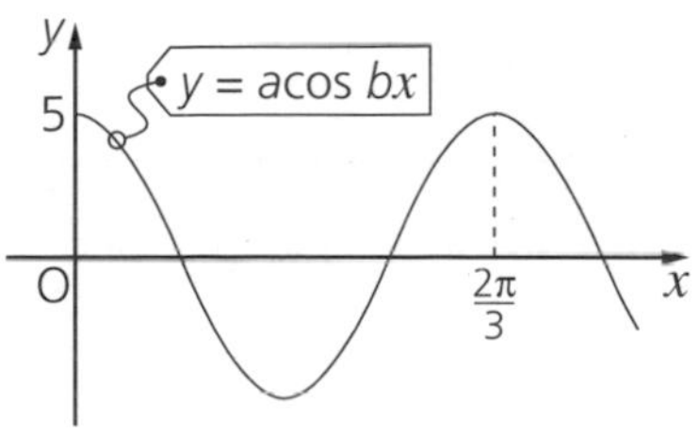

Exercise 4.5 Sketching trig graphs

page 17, example 4.4 (1st ed: page 16, example 4.2)

Sketch for $0 \le x \le 2\pi$:

1. $y = 2\cos x$ **2.** $y = \frac{1}{2}\sin 2x$ **3.** $y = \cos\left(x - \frac{\pi}{6}\right)$

4. $y = 2\sin\left(x + \frac{\pi}{3}\right)$ **5.** $y = \sin 2x + 1$ **6.** $y = \frac{1}{2}\cos 2x - 1$

5. INTRODUCTION TO DIFFERENTIATION

Exercise 5.1 The meaning of $f'(x)$

See these pages in Leckie & Leckie's *Higher Maths Course Notes:*

Each straight line shown has equation $y = f(x)$. Determine $f'(x)$.

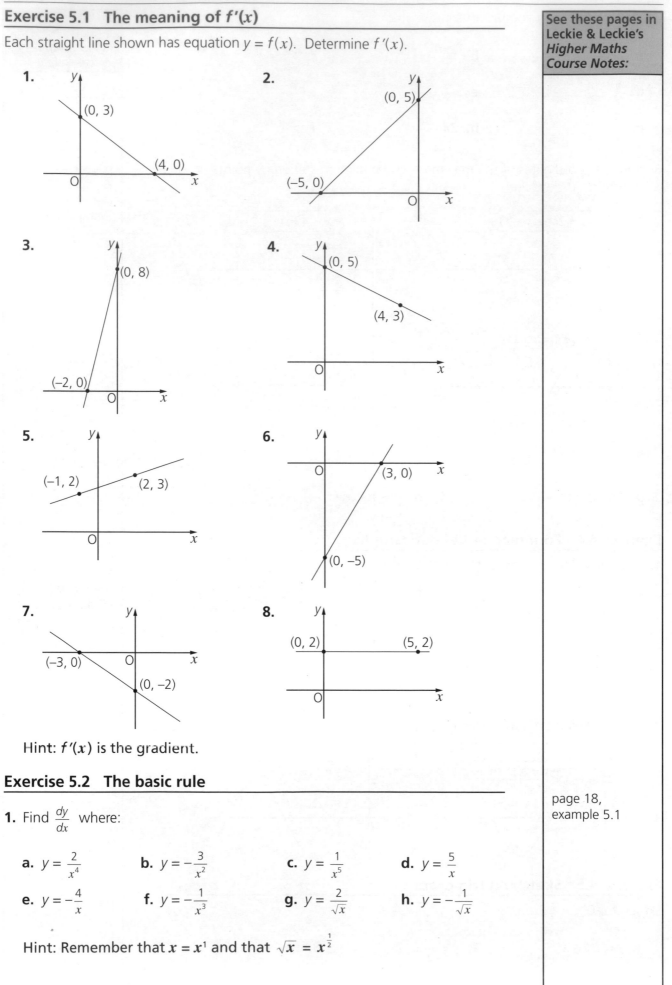

1.

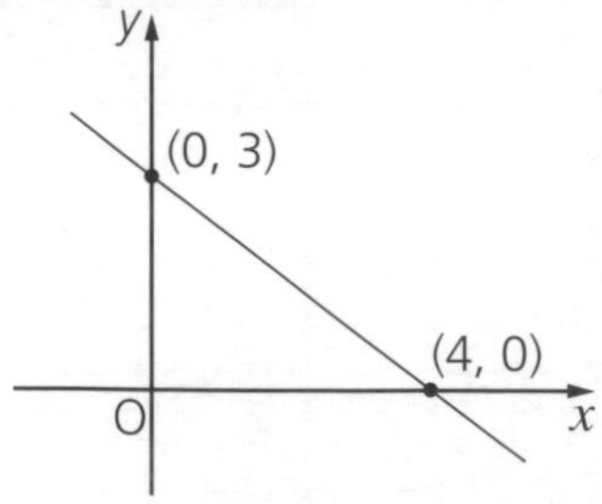

2.

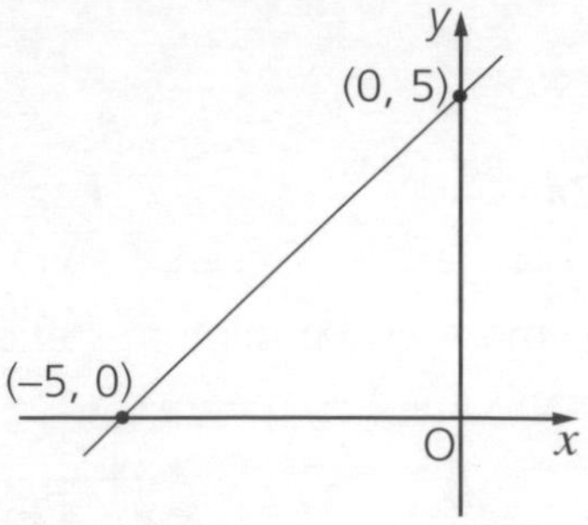

3.

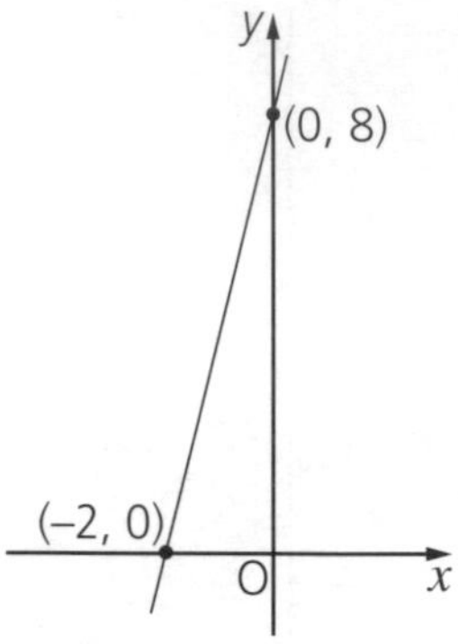

4.

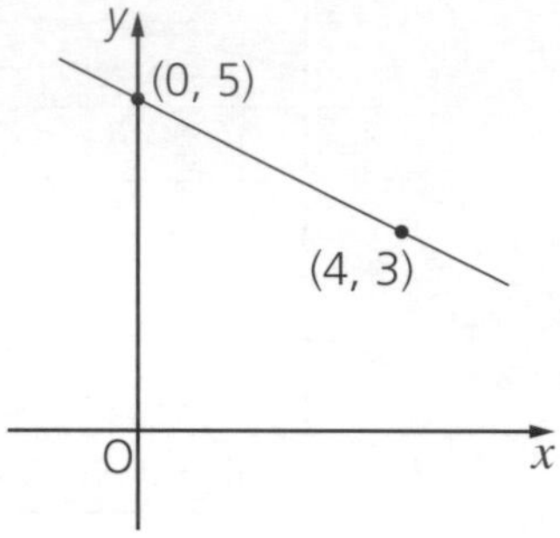

5.

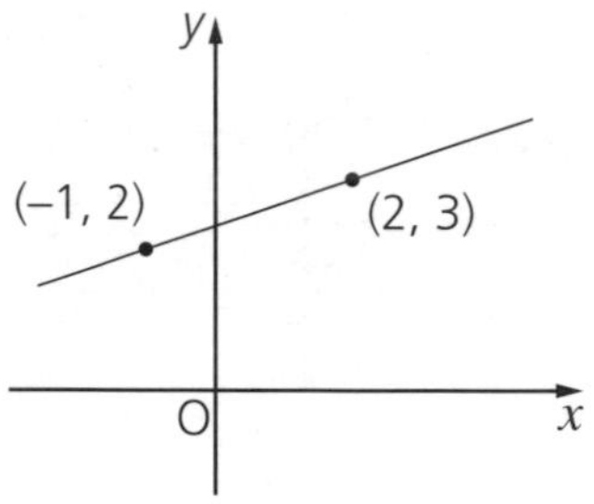

6.

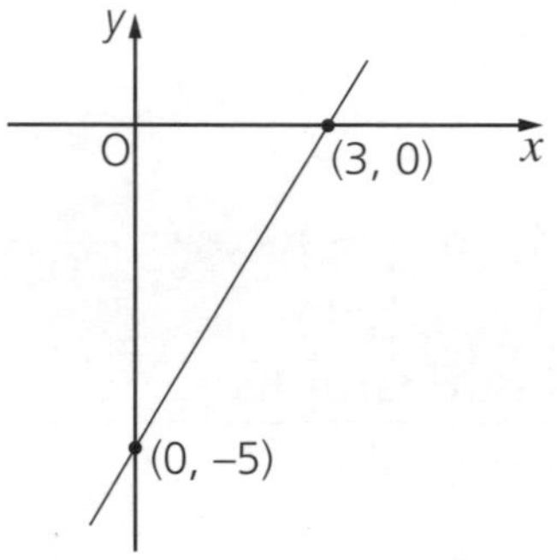

7.

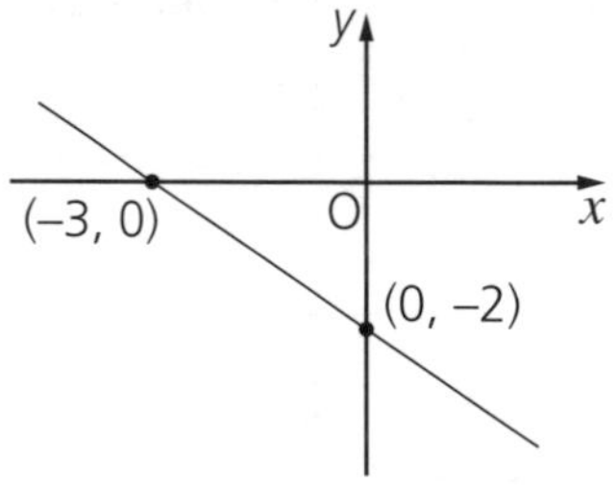

8.

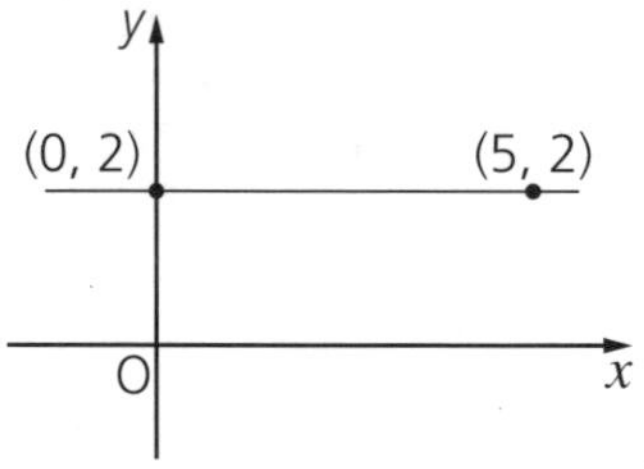

Hint: $f'(x)$ is the gradient.

Exercise 5.2 The basic rule

page 18, example 5.1

1. Find $\frac{dy}{dx}$ where:

a. $y = \frac{2}{x^4}$ **b.** $y = -\frac{3}{x^2}$ **c.** $y = \frac{1}{x^5}$ **d.** $y = \frac{5}{x}$

e. $y = -\frac{4}{x}$ **f.** $y = -\frac{1}{x^3}$ **g.** $y = \frac{2}{\sqrt{x}}$ **h.** $y = -\frac{1}{\sqrt{x}}$

Hint: Remember that $x = x^1$ and that $\sqrt{x} = x^{\frac{1}{2}}$

See these pages in Leckie & Leckie's *Higher Maths Course Notes:*

page 18, example 5.1

2. Differentiate:

a. $f(x) = x^{\frac{1}{2}} + x^{\frac{3}{2}}$ **b.** $y = -2x^{\frac{1}{2}} - x^{-\frac{1}{2}}$ **c.** $y = 5x^{-\frac{1}{2}} + 2x^{-1}$

d. $f(x) = 3x^{-2} + \frac{1}{2}x^{-1}$ **e.** $y = \frac{2}{3}x^{\frac{1}{2}} - 2x^{\frac{1}{2}}$ **f.** $f(x) = x^{-3} - x^{-2} - x^{-1}$

g. $f(x) = \frac{1}{3}x^{\frac{3}{2}} - \frac{2}{3}x^{-\frac{1}{2}}$ **h.** $f(x) = -x^{-\frac{3}{2}} - 3x^{-\frac{1}{2}}$

Exercise 5.3 Differentiating and preparing for use

See page 19 for hints.

1. Find $\frac{dy}{dx}$ where:

a. $y = \sqrt{x}$ **b.** $y = x^2\sqrt{x}$ **c.** $y = \left(\sqrt{x}\right)^3$

d. $y = \frac{x}{\sqrt{x}}$ (subtract the indices) **e.** $y = \frac{\sqrt{x}}{x}$ **f.** $y = x^3\sqrt{x}$

g. $y = \frac{1}{x\sqrt{x}}$ **h.** $y = \frac{x^2}{\sqrt{x}}$

2. Find $\frac{dy}{dx}$ where:

a. $y = \frac{4}{x^3} + \sqrt{x}$ **b.** $y = -\frac{3}{x} - x\sqrt{x}$ **c.** $y = \frac{1}{x} - \frac{x}{\sqrt{x}}$

d. $y = -\frac{5}{x^3} - x^2\sqrt{x}$ **e.** $y = x\sqrt{x} + \frac{8}{x}$ **f.** $y = \frac{\sqrt{x}}{x} - \frac{3}{x^2}$

g. $y = x\sqrt{x} - \frac{1}{x\sqrt{x}}$ **h.** $y = \frac{2x^2}{\sqrt{x}} + \frac{\sqrt{x}}{x^2}$

3. Differentiate:

a. $y = \frac{1}{x}$ **b.** $f(x) = \frac{3}{x^{\frac{1}{2}}}$ **c.** $f(x) = \frac{2}{\sqrt{x}}$

d. $y = \frac{1}{x^2} - \sqrt{x}$ **e.** $y = \frac{3x}{\sqrt{x}} - \frac{2}{x}$ **f.** $f(x) = \frac{2x+1}{\sqrt{x}}$

g. $y = \frac{1-x^2}{\sqrt{x}}$ **h.** $f(x) = \frac{3-2x}{x^2}$ **i.** $f(x) = \frac{1}{\sqrt{x}} - 2\sqrt{x}$

j. $f(x) = \frac{x+1}{\sqrt{x}}$ **k.** $y = \frac{3\sqrt{x}+x}{\sqrt{x}}$ **l.** $f(x) = \frac{\sqrt{x}-x}{x^{\frac{3}{2}}}$

m. $y = \frac{1+2x^2}{\sqrt{x}}$ **n.** $f(x) = \frac{x^3-2\sqrt{x}}{x}$ **o.** $y = \frac{\sqrt{x}-x^2}{x}$

p. $f(x) = \frac{x+1-\sqrt{x}}{3\sqrt{x}}$

Exercise 5.4 Evaluating $f'(x)$

See these pages in Leckie & Leckie's *Higher Maths Course Notes:*

page 19, example 5.2

Find:

1. $f'(4)$ where $f(x) = 5\sqrt{x} - x$

2. $f'(16)$ where $f(x) = \dfrac{\sqrt{x} - 4x^2}{\sqrt{x}}$

3. $f'(1)$ where $f(x) = \dfrac{x - \sqrt{x}}{x}$

4. $f'(9)$ where $f(x) = \dfrac{x^2 - x}{\sqrt{x}}$

5. $f'(1)$ where $f(x) = \dfrac{2 + x}{\sqrt{x}}$

6. $f'(4)$ where $f(x) = \dfrac{7\sqrt{x} - 2x}{\left(\sqrt{x}\right)^3}$

7. $f'(36)$ where $f(x) = \dfrac{2x + 3x^2}{\sqrt{x}}$

8. $f'(9)$ where $f(x) = \dfrac{18 - 3x}{2\sqrt{x}}$

Exercise 5.5 Sketching the gradient graph

Hints and an example are on page 19.

The graph of $y = f(x)$ is shown. In each case sketch the graph of $y = f'(x)$.

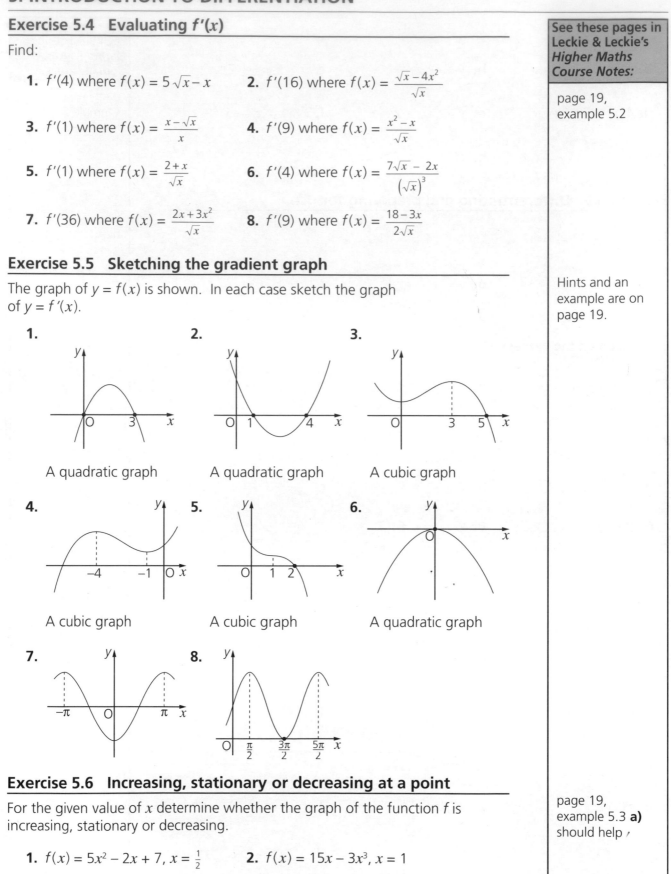

1.

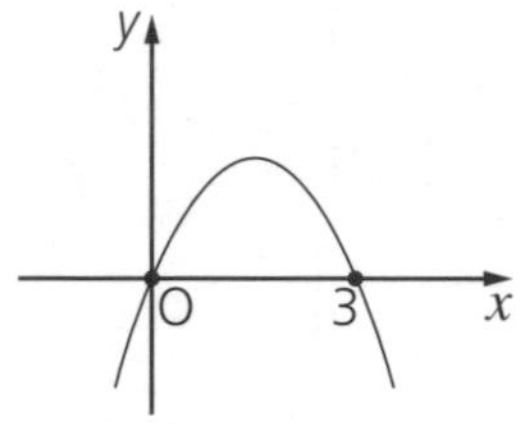

A quadratic graph

2.

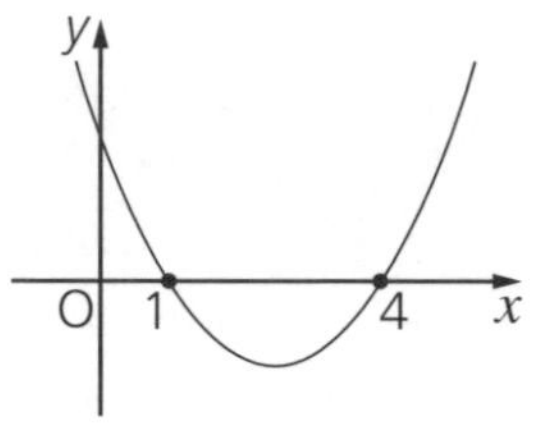

A quadratic graph

3.

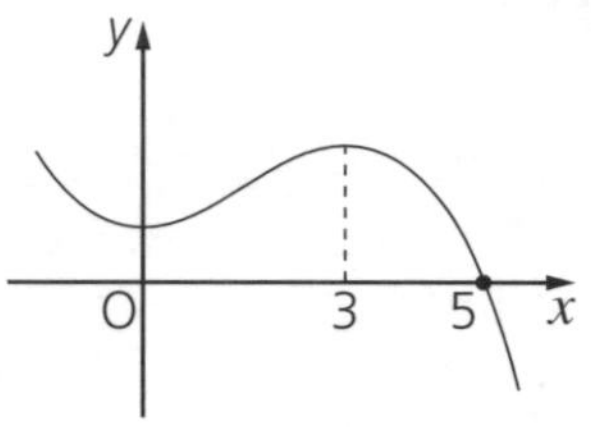

A cubic graph

4.

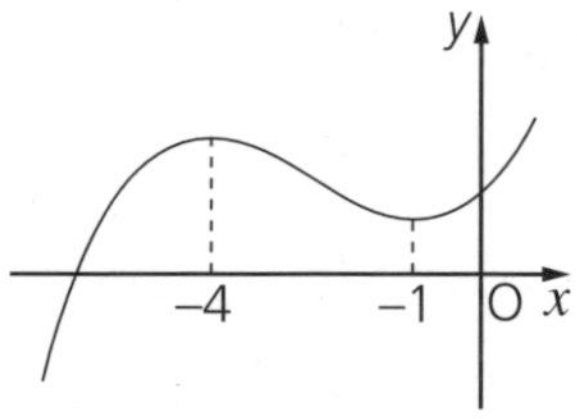

A cubic graph

5.

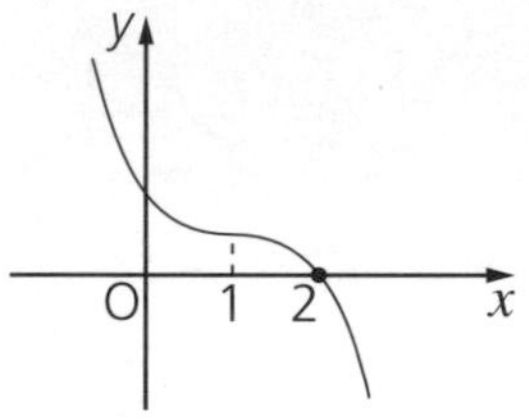

A cubic graph

6.

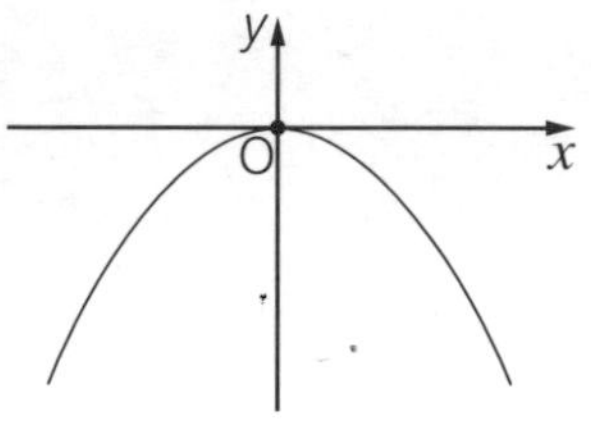

A quadratic graph

7.

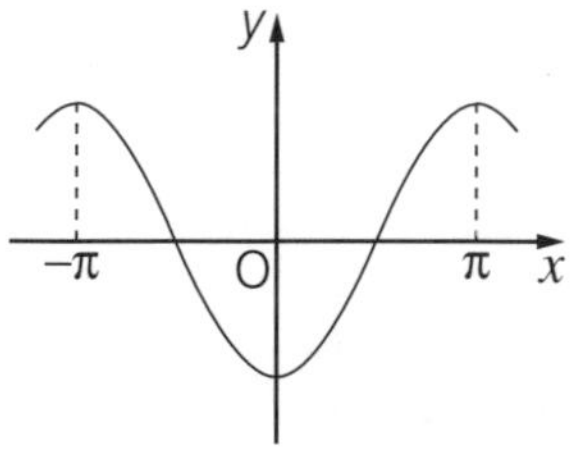

8.

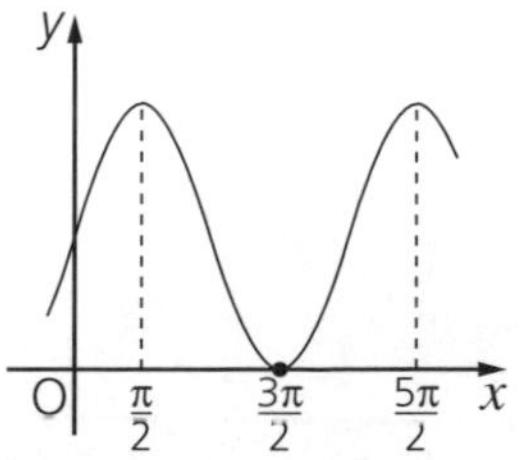

Exercise 5.6 Increasing, stationary or decreasing at a point

page 19, example 5.3 **a)** should help

For the given value of x determine whether the graph of the function f is increasing, stationary or decreasing.

1. $f(x) = 5x^2 - 2x + 7,\ x = \frac{1}{2}$

2. $f(x) = 15x - 3x^3,\ x = 1$

3. $f(x) = x^3 - 2x^2 - 6x,\ x = -1$

4. $f(x) = 5 - 3x^2 - x^3,\ x = -2$

5. $f(x) = -16x^5 - x^2,\ x = \frac{1}{2}$

6. $f(x) = 4x^3 - 2x^2 - 8x,\ x = 1$

7. $f(x) = 4x^3 - 2x^2 - 8x,\ x = \frac{1}{2}$

8. $f(x) = 4x^3 - 2x^2 - 8x,\ x = \frac{3}{2}$

Hint: Find $f'(x)$ then substitute the value of x

See these pages in Leckie & Leckie's *Higher Maths Course Notes:*

Exercise 5.7 Points with a given gradient

1. Find the coordinates of the two points on the curve $y = x^3 - 2x + 3$ where the gradient is 10.
2. There are two points on the curve $y = 2x^3 - x^2$ where the gradient is 4. Find the coordinates of these points.
3. Where on the curve $y = -\frac{2}{x}$ is the gradient $\frac{2}{9}$?
4. A tangent to the curve $y = \sqrt{x}$ has gradient $\frac{1}{3}$. Find its point of contact with the curve.

Exercise 5.8 Equations of tangents to curves

page 20, example 5.4

1. In each case find the equation of the tangent at A on the given curve:

   a. A(–1, 3), $y = 2x^2 - 3x - 2$ b. A(2, 6), $y = x^3 - 2x^2 + 3x$

   c. A(0, 7), $y = 2x^3 - 2x + 7$ d. A(–3, 1), $y = x^3 + 3x^2 - 2x - 5$

2. On the curve $y = \frac{1}{3}x^3 - 2x + 1$ tangents are drawn at the points A(–1, $\frac{8}{3}$), B(0, 1) and C(1, $-\frac{2}{3}$).

   a. Which pair of tangents are parallel?
   Hint: Find their gradients.

   b. Find the equations of the three tangents.

Exercise 5.9 Stationary points and their nature

pages 20 and 21, examples 5.5 and 5.6

Find algebraically the coordinates of the stationary points and determine their nature for these curves:

1. $y = x^3 - 9x^2 + 2$ 2. $y = x^4 + 4x^3 - 1$
3. $y = 2x^3 + 3x^2 - 12x + 2$ 4. $y = 3x^4 - 8x^3 + 6x^2$
5. $y = 4x^5 + 5x^4 - 2$ 6. $y = 3x^4 - 4x^3 - 36x^2 + 5$
7. $y = 3x^5 - 15x^4 + 20x^3$ 8. $y = 6x^4 + 8x^3 + 3x^2 + \frac{7}{8}$

Exercise 5.10 Increasing or decreasing intervals

Find algebraically the values of x for which the function...

1. $f(x) = 6x^2 - x^3$ is increasing
2. $f(x) = x^3 - 3x^2 - 9x$ is decreasing
3. $g(x) = x^3 - 9x^2 + 15x$ is increasing
4. $h(x) = 24x - 9x^2 - 2x^3$ is decreasing
5. $f(x) = x^3 + 2x^2 + x$ is stationary or decreasing
6. $g(x) = 4x + \frac{9}{2}x^2 - 3x^3$ is stationary or increasing
7. $h(x) = -2x^3 + \frac{11}{2}x^2 - 4x$ is decreasing
8. $f(x) = 5x^3 + 7x^2 - 8x$ is increasing or stationary

Hint: Construct a Table of Signs first and then use it to determine the required intervals.

Exercise 5.11 Rates of Change

See these pages in Leckie & Leckie's *Higher Maths Course Notes:*

page 22, example 5.8

1. Three stones are thrown up into the air at the same time. The height h metres of the stones t seconds after they are thrown up is given by these formulae:

   Stone 1: $h = 60t - 5t^2$ Stone 2: $h = 56t - 7t^2$ Stone 3: $h = 16t - 4t^2$

   For each stone find its speed:

   a. when it is thrown

   b. after 2 seconds

   c. after 4 seconds.

2. A firework is launched. The height h metres of the firework t minutes after launch is given by the formula $h = 400t - 200t^2$.

   a. Find its speed at launch.

   b. Find its speed after 1 minute and explain your answer.

   c. Compare its speed after 2 minutes with its speed at launch and explain your result.

Exercise 6.1 n^{th} Term Formula and Recurrence Relations

See these pages in Leckie & Leckie's *Higher Maths Course Notes:* page 23, example 6.1

1. For each nth term formula calculate u_5, the 5th term:

a. $u_n = 2^n$ **b.** $u_n = 3n + 1$ **c.** $u_n = 10 - 2n$

d. $u_n = n^2 - 3$ **e.** $u_n = 3^{n-2}$ **f.** $u_n = 4n^2 - 5$

g. $u_n = 2n + 1$ **h.** $u_n = 2^n + 1$ **i.** $u_n = 2^{n+1}$

2. For each recurrence relation calculate u_5, the 5th term:

a. $u_{n+1} = 2u_n$ with $u_1 = 1$ **b.** $u_{n+1} = \frac{1}{2}u_n + 4$ with $u_1 = 24$

c. $u_{n+1} = 12 - 2u_n$ with $u_1 = 3$ **d.** $u_{n+1} = \frac{1}{2}u_n$ with $u_1 = 256$

e. $u_{n+1} = 3u_n - 1$ with $u_1 = 1$ **f.** $u_{n+1} = u_n + 10$ with $u_1 = 2$

Exercise 6.2 Existence of a limit

page 24, example 6.4 **a)**

Which of the sequences defined by these recurrence relations have a limit? Explain why.

1. $u_{n+1} = 0{\cdot}8u_n - 2$ **2.** $u_{n+1} = 1{\cdot}1u_n + 3$ **3.** $u_{n+1} = 4 + 2u_n$

4. $u_{n+1} = 3 - \frac{1}{2}u_n$ **5.** $u_{n+1} = \frac{3}{2}u_n - \frac{1}{2}$ **6.** $u_{n+1} = 5 + \frac{u_n}{3}$

7. $3u_{n+1} = 2u_n + 6$ **8.** $2u_{n+1} - 3u_n = 1$

Exercise 6.3 Calculation of limit

page 24, example 6.4 **b)**

For the sequence defined by each recurrence relation explain whether or not there is a limit as n tends to infinity. If there is a limit then find its **exact** value.

1. $u_{n+1} = 0{\cdot}4u_n + 1$ **2.** $u_{n+1} = 0{\cdot}7u_n + 8$ **3.** $2u_{n+1} = 3u_n + 8$

4. $u_{n+1} = \frac{u_n}{4} + 5$ **5.** $7u_{n+1} = 2u_n + 8$ **6.** $u_{n+1} = \frac{1}{3}u_n - 1$

7. $11(u_{n+1} - 1) = 4u_n$ **8.** $23u_{n+1} - 14u_n = 46$

Exercise 6.4 Problems in context

page 24, example 6.5

1. Birds each day eat 5% of the seeds stored in a barn so the farmer then tops them up with a further 3 kg of seeds. Initially there were 100 kg of seeds. In the long term what weight of seeds will there be?

2. 60% of pollutant is removed each day by a water-purifying machine but 10 litres of new pollutant is then added. If the water initially contained 20 litres of pollutant what will be the long-term level?

3. 15% of an ant colony dies each day but then 150 new ants are born each night. If the colony starts with 500 ants what is its final size?

4. The body destroys 70% of a drug in a day so a daily 28 unit injection is then given. The initial injection was 50 units.

   a. At no time should the body contain more than 50 units of the drug. Is this course of treatment safe?

   b. Is it safe to increase the daily injections to 36 units?

5. The air pressure in a Bouncy Castle reduces by 12% from a day's use so the owners increase the pressure by 9 units for the next day. Initially the pressure was 70 units and it is dangerous to operate at greater than 74·5 units pressure. Is what they are doing safe?

Exercise 7.1 Zero remainder means a factor

See these pages in Leckie & Leckie's *Higher Maths Course Notes:*

page 26, example 7.3 **a)**

1. Show that in each case the given expression is a factor of $f(x)$.

   a. $x + 1$; $f(x) = x^3 - 6x^2 + 3x + 10$ b. $x - 2$; $f(x) = x^3 - x^2 + x - 6$

   c. $x + 4$; $f(x) = 4x^3 + 16x^2 - x - 4$ d. $x - 1$; $f(x) = x^3 - 7x + 6$

2. Show that $x + 2$ and $x - 4$ are both factors of $f(x) = x^4 - 15x^2 - 10x + 24$

Exercise 7.2 Fully factorised form

page 26, example 7.3 **a)**

1. Show that the given expression is a factor of $f(x)$ and hence express $f(x)$ in fully factorised form.

   a. $x - 3$; $f(x) = x^3 - x^2 - 5x - 3$ b. $x - 1$; $f(x) = x^3 - 6x^2 + 11x - 6$

   c. $x - 2$; $f(x) = x^3 - 7x + 6$ d. $x - 1$; $f(x) = 6x^3 - 5x^2 - 2x + 1$

   e. $x + 2$; $f(x) = x^3 - 3x + 2$ f. $x + 1$; $f(x) = 4x^3 + 4x^2 - x - 1$

   g. $x + 3$; $f(x) = 2x^3 + 7x^2 + 2x - 3$

2. a. Show that $x - 1$ is a factor of $f(x) = 2x^4 - 3x^3 - x^2 + 3x - 1$.

   b. Hence factorise $f(x)$ into two factors.

   c. Now show that $x + 1$ is a factor of one of these factors.

   d. Hence express $f(x)$ in fully factorised form.

3. In each case by finding a factor of the expression write it in factorised form.

   a. $4x^3 - 4x^2 - x + 1$ b. $x^3 - 2x - 1$ c. $x^3 - 6x^2 + 12x - 8$

   d. $6x^3 + 13x^2 + x - 2$ e. $2x^3 - 9x^2 + 8x + 3$ f. $2x^3 - 3x + 10$

   g. $x^3 - 8$ h. $x^3 + 27$

Exercise 7.3 Solving equations and applications

page 26, example 7.3 **b)**

1. Solve these equations:

   a. $x^4 + x = 0$ b. $y^3 - 7y + 6 = 0$ c. $2x^3 - 9x^2 + 7x + 6 = 0$

   d. $3t^5 - 6t^3 + 3t = 0$ e. $6x^3 - 7x^2 - x + 2 = 0$ f. $4y^3 - 12y^2 - y + 3 = 0$

   g. $2x^4 - 16x^2 + 6x = 0$

2. Find the coordinates of the points of intersection of the following lines and curves:

   a. $y = 2x + 3$; $y = x^3 - 5x^2 + 10x - 1$ b. $y = 3x - 1$; $y = x^3 + x^2 - x - 5$

   c. $y = -2x + 10$; $y = x^3 + 4x^2 - 5x - 8$ d. $y = x + 2$; $y = x^3 + 2x^2 - 8x - 16$

   Hint: Set them equal to each other and solve the resulting equation.

3. A furniture designer has created a 'lounger' modelled by the curve $y = x^3 + 3x^2 - x - 6$. The arm-rest is modelled by the tangent to the curve at the point C(–2, 0).

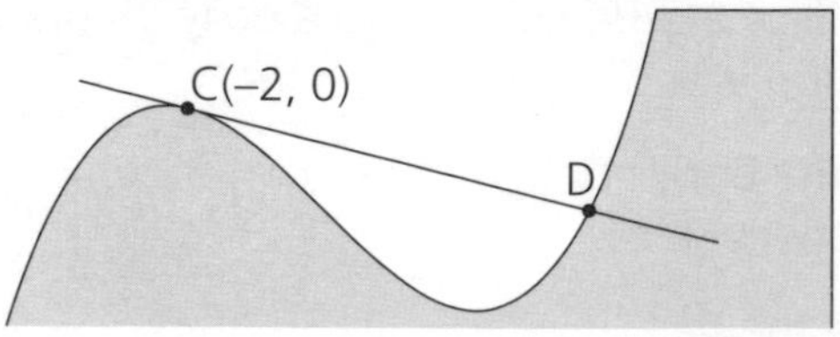

   Find the coordinates of D, the point where the arm-rest is attached to the back of the lounger.

   Hint: First use the ideas from Exercise 5.8 on page 17 of this book.

See these pages in Leckie & Leckie's *Higher Maths Course Notes:*

Exercise 8.1 Sketching quadratic graphs

Sketch the following graphs showing clearly the x-intercepts (the points where the graph crosses the x-axis).

1. $y = x^2 - 3x$ **2.** $y = x^2 + 4x - 5$ **3.** $y = x^2 + 2x$

4. $y = 5 + 4x - x^2$ **5.** $y = 4x^2 - 1$ **6.** $y = 2 + 3x - 2x^2$

7. $y = 4x^2 + 4x - 15$ **8.** $y = -2x^2 - 7x$

Hint: Set $y = 0$ for x-intercepts. Positive x^2:  Negative x^2: 

Exercise 8.2 Using the discriminant

page 27, example 8.1

Use the discriminant to determine the nature of the roots of these quadratic equations:

1. $2x^2 + x + 1 = 0$ **2.** $2x^2 + x - 1 = 0$ **3.** $4x^2 - 4x + 1 = 0$

4. $x^2 + 6x + 9 = 0$ **5.** $x^2 - x + 6 = 0$ **6.** $3x^2 + 3x - 1 = 0$

7. $9x^2 - 12x + 4 = 0$ **8.** $x^2 - 11x - 31 = 0$

Exercise 8.3 Equal roots

page 27, example 8.1 **b)**

1. Which of these equations have equal roots?

a. $x^2 - 2x + 1 = 0$ **b.** $4x^2 + 4x + 1 = 0$ **c.** $4x^2 - 6x + 2 = 0$

d. $x^2 + 8x + 16 = 0$ **e.** $9x^2 - 6x - 1 = 0$ **f.** $4x^2 + 8x + 3 = 0$

g. $25x^2 - 40x + 16 = 0$ **h.** $9x^2 + 24x + 16 = 0$

page 28, example 8.2 and example 8.3

2. Use the discriminant to show that the given line is a tangent to the curve:

a. $y = 2x - 9$ and $y = 4x^2 + 14x$ **b.** $y = 3x + 2$ and $y = x^2 - 11x + 51$

c. $y = 10x - 1$ and $y = 25x^2$ **d.** $y + 2x = 5$ and $x^2 + y^2 = 5$

e. $x + 2y = 7$ and $x^2 + y^2 - 2x + 4y - 15 = 0$

Exercise 8.4 Conditions on the roots

page 28, example 8.5

1. These equations have equal roots. Find the value of a, b or c in each case.

a. $ax^2 + 4x + 2 = 0$ **b.** $ax^2 + x + 1 = 0$ **c.** $ax^2 - 3x + 3 = 0$

d. $3x^2 - 2x + c = 0$ **e.** $2x^2 + 4x + c = 0$ **f.** $-3x^2 - 6x + c = 0$

g. $2x^2 + bx + 8 = 0$ (two possibilities) **h.** $-x^2 + bx - 4 = 0$ (two possibilities)

2. These equations have equal roots. Find the possible values for k in each case.

a. $kx^2 + kx + 2 = 0$ **b.** $x^2 + (k - 1)x - k = 0$

c. $(2k + 1)x^2 + (2k + 1)x + 1 = 0$ **d.** $x(x + k) = -4$

e. $x(x - k) = k$ **f.** $(x + k)^2 + x^2 = 2$

g. $k - (2x - k)^2 = 2$ **h.** $(x - k)^2 + (2x - k)^2 = 5$

3. For what values of k does:

a. $4x^2 + 8x + k = 0$ have real roots

b. $kx^2 - 2x + 3 = 0$ have no real roots

c. $2x^2 + kx + 2 = 0$ have equal roots

d. $kx^2 - 3x + k = 0$ have real roots

e. $\frac{4(x-1)}{x^2+3} = k$ have equal roots?

Exercise 8.5 Quadratic inequalities

Solve the following inequalities using the graphs:

1.

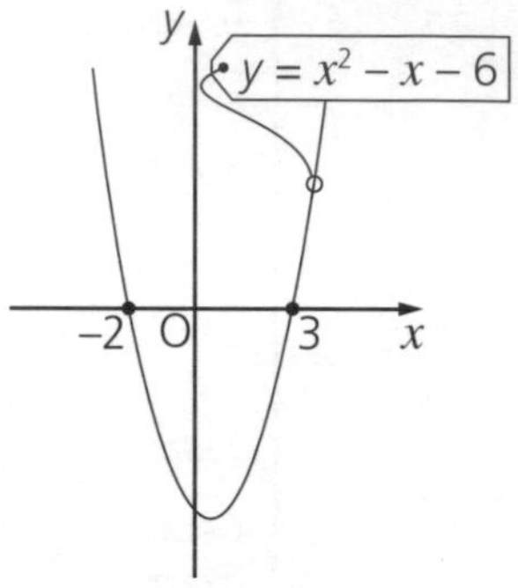

$x^2 - x - 6 \leq 0$

2.

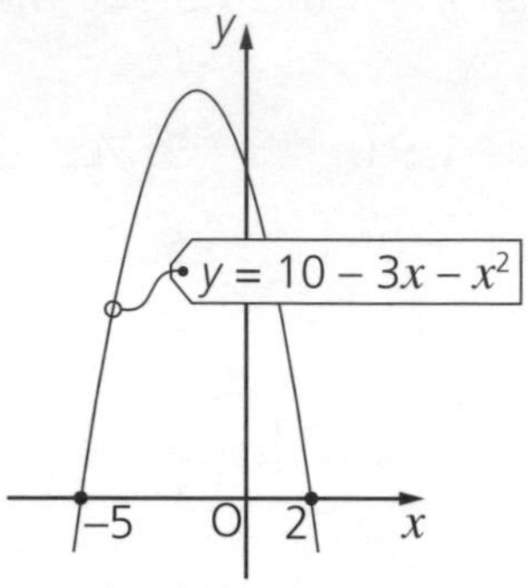

$10 - 3x - x^2 > 0$

3.

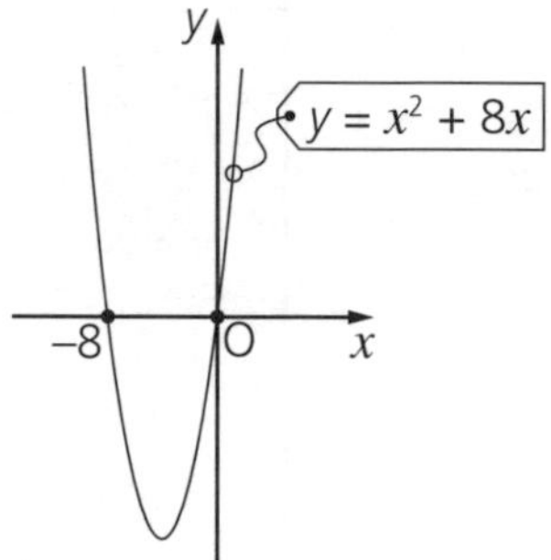

$x^2 + 8x > 0$

4.

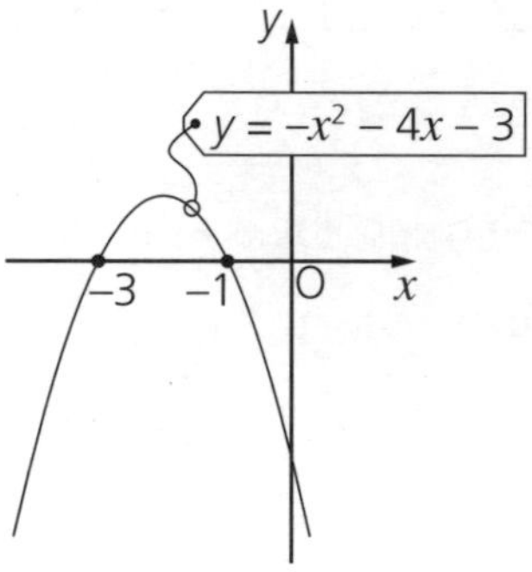

$-x^2 - 4x - 3 \leq 0$

5.

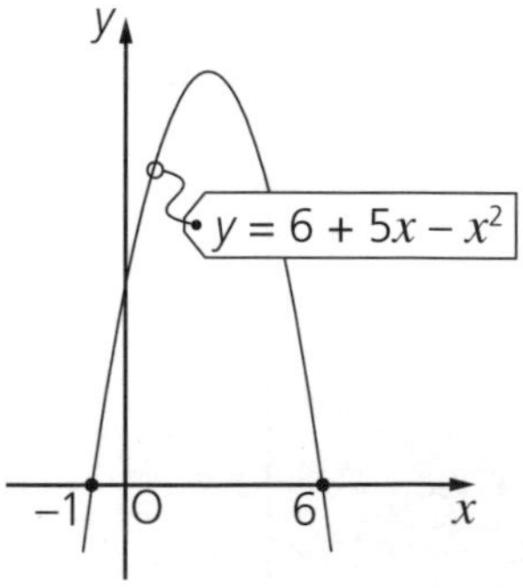

$6 + 5x - x^2 \geq 0$

6.

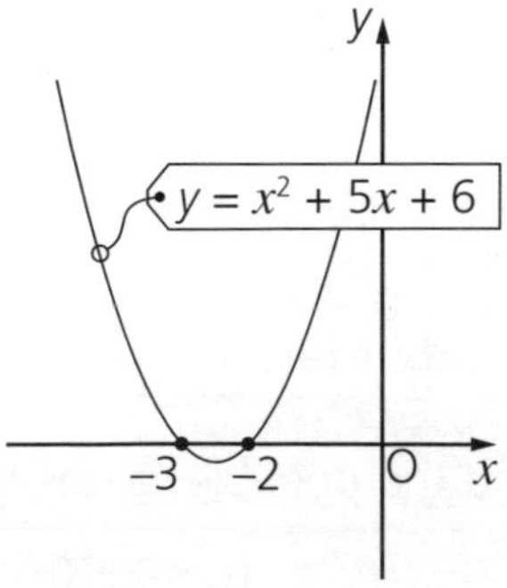

$x^2 + 5x + 6 \geq 0$

7. $x^2 + x - 12 \leq 0$

8. $20 + x - x^2 > 0$

9. $6 - x - x^2 < 0$

10. $6x^2 - 13x + 6 \geq 0$

See these pages in Leckie & Leckie's *Higher Maths Course Notes:*

page 28, example 8.4 and example 8.5

page 29, example 8.6

Exercise 9.1 Integrating integral powers of x

See these pages in Leckie & Leckie's Higher Maths Course Notes: page 31, example 9.1

1. Find:

a. $\int x^3\,dx$ **b.** $\int 4x\,dx$ (Hint: x is x^1) **c.** $\int 5x^4\,dx$

d. $\int 6x^2\,dx$ **e.** $\int x^2\,dx$ **f.** $\int -3x^2\,dx$

g. $\int -10x^4\,dx$ **h.** $\int 5x^2\,dx$

2. Find:

a. $\int \frac{1}{x^2}\,dx$ **b.** $\int \frac{5}{x^3}\,dx$ **c.** $\int -\frac{3}{x^2}\,dx$

d. $\int \frac{5}{2x^2}\,dx$ **e.** $\int \frac{1}{3x^4}\,dx$ **f.** $\int -\frac{2}{5x^3}\,dx$

3. Find:

a. $\int \left(x - \frac{2}{x^2}\right)dx$ **b.** $\int \left(\frac{1}{x^3} - 2x^2\right)dx$ **c.** $\int \left(5x - \frac{5}{x^6}\right)dx$

d. $\int \left(\frac{4}{x^3} + \frac{3}{x^4}\right)dx$ **e.** $\int \left(\frac{3}{2x^2} + \frac{5}{3x^6}\right)dx$ **f.** $\int \left(5x^2 + 5 - \frac{3}{2x^2}\right)dx$

Exercise 9.2 Integrating fractional powers of x

page 31, example 9.2

1. Find:

a. $\int x^{\frac{1}{2}}\,dx$ **b.** $\int 3x^{\frac{1}{2}}\,dx$ **c.** $\int 2x^{-\frac{1}{2}}\,dx$

d. $\int \frac{5x^{\frac{1}{2}}}{2}\,dx$ **e.** $\int \frac{x^{-\frac{1}{2}}}{2}\,dx$ **f.** $\int \frac{1}{3x^{\frac{1}{2}}}\,dx$

2. Find:

a. $\int 5\sqrt{x}\,dx$ **b.** $\int \frac{4}{\sqrt{x}}\,dx$ **c.** $\int \left(x - \frac{1}{\sqrt{x}}\right)dx$

d. $\int \left(\frac{2}{3\sqrt{x}} + \sqrt{x}\right)dx$ **e.** $\int \left(6\sqrt{x} - \frac{6}{\sqrt{x}}\right)dx$ **f.** $\int x\left(1 - \sqrt{x}\right)dx$

Exercise 9.3 Definite Integrals

page 32, example 9.3

Evaluate:

1. $\int_0^2 x\,dx$ **2.** $\int_1^2 3\,dx$ **3.** $\int_{-1}^1 (2x-1)\,dx$

4. $\int_{-2}^1 (5\quad 3x)\,dx$ **5.** $\int_1^3 3x^2\,dx$ **6.** $\int_0^1 \left(x^2 - x + 2\right)dx$

Exercise 9.4 Definite Integrals and Exact Values

See these pages in Leckie & Leckie's *Higher Maths Course Notes:*

page 32, example 9.4

Find the exact value of:

1. $\int_9^{25} \frac{1}{\sqrt{x}}\,dx$
2. $\int_4^9 3\sqrt{x}\,dx$
3. $\int_1^9 \frac{3}{2\sqrt{x}}\,dx$
4. $\int_4^9 \left(\sqrt{x} - \frac{1}{\sqrt{x}}\right) dx$
5. $\int_0^4 \sqrt{x}\left(\sqrt{x} - 1\right) dx$
6. $\int_1^4 \left(\sqrt{x} + \frac{1}{\sqrt{x}}\right) dx$
7. $\int_1^9 \left(\frac{1}{x^2} + \sqrt{x}\right) dx$
8. $\int_1^4 \left(\frac{4}{x^3} + \frac{1}{2\sqrt{x}}\right) dx$

Exercise 9.5 Area cut off by the x-axis

page 32, example 9.5

Find the area enclosed by the x-axis and each of these curves:

1. $y = 3 - 3x^2$
2. $y = 3x^2 - 6x$
3. $y = x^2 - 2x - 3$
4. $y = 2 - x - x^2$

Exercise 9.6 Area between two curves

page 33, example 9.6

1. Find the shaded area:

a.

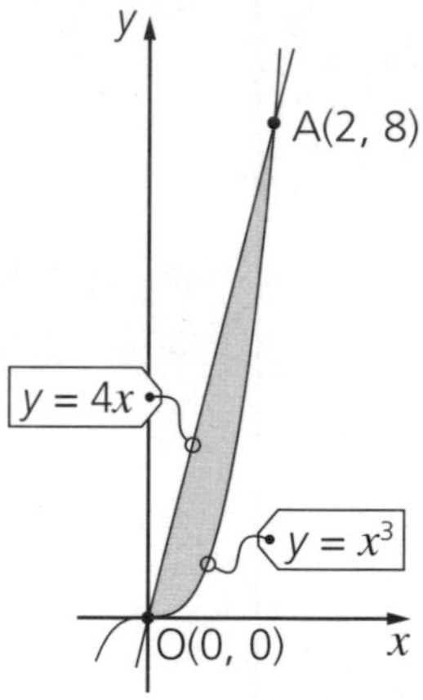

b.

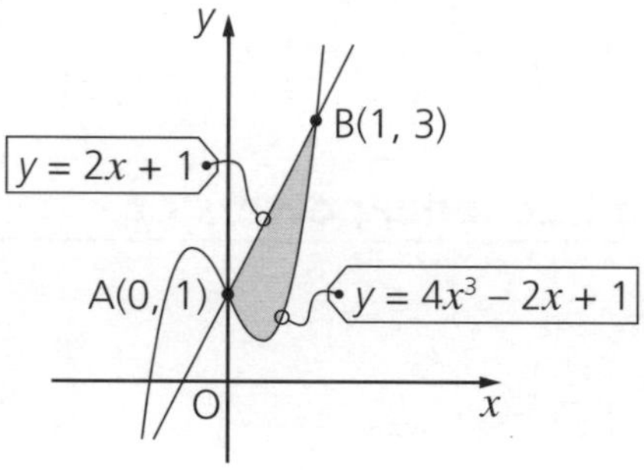

c.

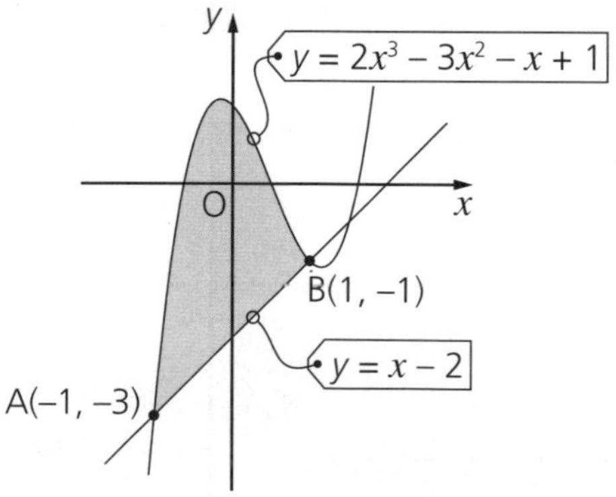

2. Find the area enclosed by these lines and curves:

a. $y = x^2$
$y = x + 2$

b. $y = 2x + 4$
$y = 4 - x^2$

c. $y = 3x^2$
$y = 9x - 6$

d. $y = \sqrt{x}$
$y = \frac{1}{2}x$

e. $y = (x - 2)^2$
$y = -2x + 4$

f. $y = 9 - x^2$
$y = x + 3$

See these pages in Leckie & Leckie's *Higher Maths Course Notes:*

Exercise 10.1 Introductory steps for solving equations

1. State the quadrant for angle x:

page 34. See step 2 of 'Solving Trig Equations' (1st ed: page 16).

a. $\sin x = 0{\cdot}2$ **b.** $\tan x = -1$ **c.** $\cos x = \frac{1}{2}$

d. $\sin x = -\frac{1}{\sqrt{2}}$ **e.** $\cos x = \frac{\sqrt{3}}{2}$ **f.** $\tan x = \frac{1}{\sqrt{3}}$

g. $\sin x = +\frac{\sqrt{3}}{2}$ **h.** $\cos x = \pm\frac{1}{\sqrt{2}}$ **i.** $\tan x = \pm\sqrt{3}$

Deg Mode

2. Find the 1st quadrant angle (to 1 decimal place) used when solving:

page 34. See step 3 of 'Solving Trig Equations' (1st ed: page 16).

a. $\sin x^\circ = -\frac{1}{3}$ **b.** $\cos x^\circ = -0{\cdot}1$ **c.** $\cos x^\circ = \frac{2}{3}$

d. $\tan x^\circ = -\frac{3}{2}$ **e.** $\sin x^\circ = -\frac{\sqrt{3}}{7}$ **f.** $\cos x^\circ = -\frac{\sqrt{2}}{3}$

Rad Mode

3. Find the 1st quadrant angle (to 3 sig figs) used when solving:

a. $\sin x = -0{\cdot}2$ **b.** $\cos x = -0{\cdot}9$ **c.** $\tan x = \frac{7}{5}$

d. $\tan x = -\sqrt{3}$ **e.** $\cos x = -\frac{1}{\sqrt{5}}$ **f.** $\sin x = -\frac{2}{9}$

4. Find the required angles using the given 1st quadrant angle:

page 34. See step 4 of 'Solving Trig Equations' (1st ed: page 16).

	1st quadrant angle	*Required angles*
a.	30°	3rd & 4th quadrants
b.	60°	1st & 4th quadrants
c.	45°	2nd & 3rd quadrants
d.	23·6°	2nd & 4th quadrants
e.	80·1°	all 4 quadrants
f.	12·9°	3rd & 4th quadrants

Exercise 10.2 Solving basic equations

Mode?

1. Solve for $0 \leq x \leq 360$ (to 1 decimal place where necessary):

page 34. Follow steps 2–4 of 'Solving Trig Equations' (1st ed: page 16).

a. $\sin x^\circ = \frac{1}{3}$ **b.** $\cos x^\circ = -\frac{1}{2}$ **c.** $\cos x^\circ = \frac{2}{3}$ **d.** $\sin x^\circ = -\frac{1}{2}$

e. $\sin x^\circ = \frac{1}{2}$ **f.** $\sin x^\circ = -\frac{1}{4}$ **g.** $\cos x^\circ = -\frac{3}{4}$ **h.** $\cos x^\circ = -\frac{1}{5}$

Mode?

2. Solve for $0 \leq x \leq 2\pi$ (to 3 sig figs):

a. $\sin x = 0{\cdot}1$ **b.** $\cos x = \frac{1}{3}$ **c.** $\tan x = -\frac{1}{2}$

d. $\sin x = -\frac{2}{3}$ **e.** $\cos x = -0{\cdot}92$ **f.** $\tan x = \sqrt{5}$

Exercise 10.3 Rearranging and solving

See these pages in Leckie & Leckie's *Higher Maths Course Notes:*

1. Find the exact value of $\sin x$, $\cos x$ or $\tan x$:

a. $2\sin x - 1 = 0$ **b.** $2\cos x - \sqrt{3} = 0$ **c.** $1 + \sqrt{2}\cos x = 0$

d. $2\sin x + 1 = 0$ **e.** $2\sin x + \sqrt{3} = 0$ **f.** $\tan x + \sqrt{3} = 0$

g. $3\tan^2 x = 1$ **h.** $\tan^2 x - 3 = 0$ **i.** $4\cos^2 x - 1 = 0$

j. $2\cos^2 x = 1$ **k.** $3 - 4\sin^2 x = 0$

Hint: For part g. onwards there are two possibilities!

page 34. See step 1 of 'Solving Trig Equations' (1st ed: page 16).

2. Solve for $0 \leq x \leq 360$ (to 1 decimal place where necessary):

a. $3\sin x° + 1 = 0$ **b.** $5\cos x° - 1 = 0$ **c.** $3\tan x° + 4 = 0$

d. $5\sin x° - \sqrt{2} = 0$ **e.** $2 - 3\cos x° = 0$ **f.** $\sqrt{5}\tan x° + 1 = 0$

g. $2\tan^2 x° - 1 = 0$ **h.** $4\sin^2 x° - 3 = 0$

page 34. Follow steps 1–4 of 'Solving Trig Equations' (1st ed: page 16).

3. Solve for $0 \leq x \leq 2\pi$ (to 3 sig figs):

a. $3\sin x + 1 = 0$ **b.** $3\cos x - 2 = 0$ **c.** $\sqrt{3}\tan x + 2 = 0$

d. $3\sin^2 x - 1 = 0$ **e.** $5\cos^2 x - 4 = 0$ **f.** $9\tan^2 x - 16 = 0$

Exercise 10.4 Exact Values

1. Simplify the following radian expressions:

a. $\pi + \frac{\pi}{4}$ (Hint: π is 4 lots of $\frac{\pi}{4}$) **b.** $\pi - \frac{\pi}{3}$ **c.** $2\pi + \frac{\pi}{6}$

d. $2\pi - \frac{\pi}{3}$ **e.** $\pi - \frac{\pi}{4}$ **f.** $2\pi - \frac{\pi}{4}$ **g.** $\pi + \frac{\pi}{3}$

h. $\pi + \frac{\pi}{6}$ **i.** $2\pi - \frac{\pi}{6}$ **j.** $2\pi + \frac{\pi}{4}$

2. Find the exact solutions of these equations for $0 \leq x \leq 2\pi$:

a. $\sin x = -\frac{\sqrt{3}}{2}$ **b.** $\tan x = \sqrt{3}$ **c.** $\cos x = -\frac{1}{\sqrt{2}}$ **d.** $\sin x = -\frac{1}{2}$

e. $\sqrt{3}\tan x = 1$ **f.** $\sqrt{2}\sin x = -1$ **g.** $2\cos x = -\sqrt{3}$ **h.** $2\cos x + 1 = 0$

page 34, example 10.1 (1st ed: page 16, example 4.3)

3. Solve each equation for $0 \leq x \leq 2\pi$, giving the exact solutions:

a. $4\cos^2 x = 1$ **b.** $2\sin^2 x = 1$ **c.** $\tan^2 x - 1 = 0$

d. $4\cos^2 x - 3 = 0$ **e.** $3\tan^2 x - 1 = 0$ **f.** $1 - 4\sin^2 x = 0$

Exercise 10.5 Multiple and other angles

1. Solve for $0 \leq x \leq 2\pi$:

a. $\sin 2x = 1$ **b.** $\cos 2x = 0$ **c.** $\sin 3x = -1$ **d.** $\sin^2 2x = 1$

e. $\cos^2 3x = 1$ **f.** $\sin 2x = \frac{1}{2}$ **g.** $\cos 2x = -\frac{1}{2}$ **h.** $\tan^2 2x = 1$

page 34, example 10.2 (1st ed: page 17, example 4.4)

2. For each diagram find algebraically the coordinates of P and Q, the points of intersection of the two graphs.

a.
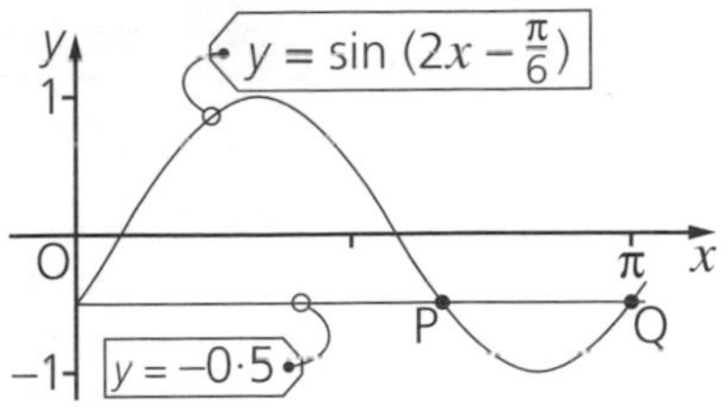

b.
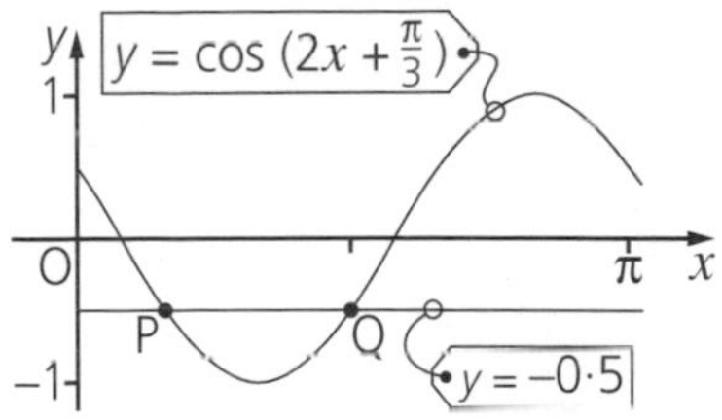

c.
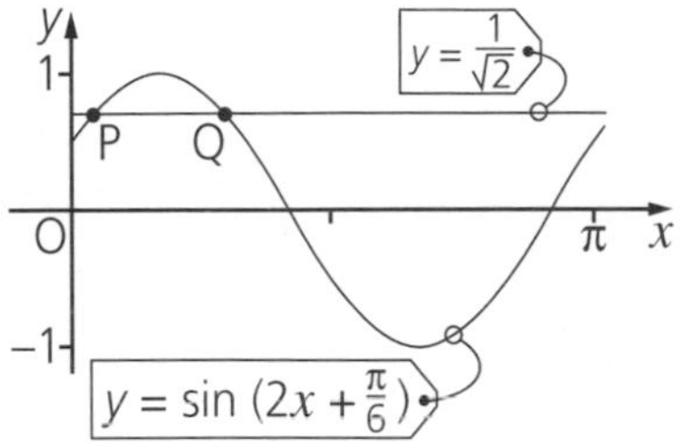

d.
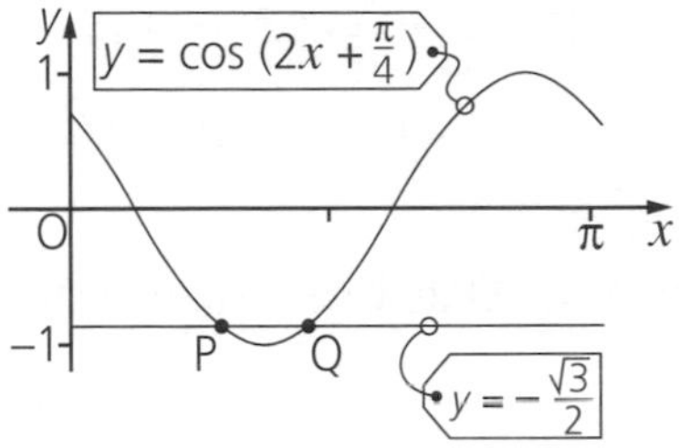

See these pages in Leckie & Leckie's *Higher Maths Course Notes:*

page 34, as example 10.3 with exact values only (1st ed: page 17, example 4.5).

Exercise 10.6 Quadratic equations

page 35. See the example discussed at the top of the page (1st ed: page 17, at the bottom of the page).

Solve for $0 \le x \le 360$ (to 1 decimal place where necessary):

1. $4\cos^2 x° + 4\cos x° - 3 = 0$
2. $2\cos^2 x° - 3\cos x° + 1 = 0$
3. $2\sin^2 x° + 3\sin x° + 1 = 0$
4. $2\sin^2 x° - \sin x° - 1 = 0$
5. $3\cos^2 x° + \cos x° = 0$
   Hint: common factor
6. $3\sin^2 x° - 2\sin x° = 0$
7. $3\cos^2 x° - 5\cos x° - 2 = 0$
8. $5\sin^2 x° + 4\sin x° - 1 = 0$

Exercise 10.7 The Addition Formulae and applications

page 35, example 10.4 (1st ed: page 35, example 10.3)

1. Expand these and simplify if possible. (Don't look at the formulae! Try to remember them!!)

a. $\cos(C - D)°$ **b.** $\sin(\theta + \phi)$ **c.** $\cos(2x + \frac{\pi}{6})$ **d.** $\sin(x - \pi)$

(θ = theta, ϕ = phi)

e. $\cos(180 - x)°$ **f.** $\cos(45 + 3x)°$ **g.** $\sin(\frac{x}{2} - 45)°$ **h.** $\sin(\frac{\pi}{3} + \frac{x}{2})$

page 35, example 10.5 (1st ed: page 35, example 10.4)

2. a.
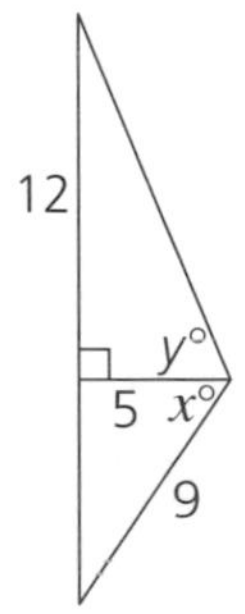

Show that the exact value of $\sin(x + y)°$ is $\frac{10\sqrt{14} + 60}{117}$

b.
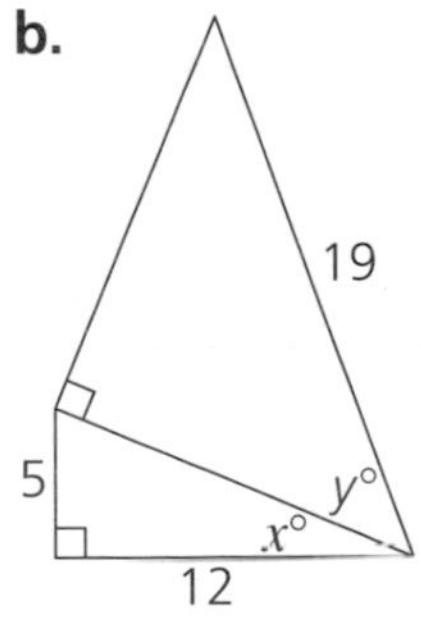

Show that the exact value of $\cos(x + y)°$ is $\frac{156 - 40\sqrt{3}}{247}$

c.
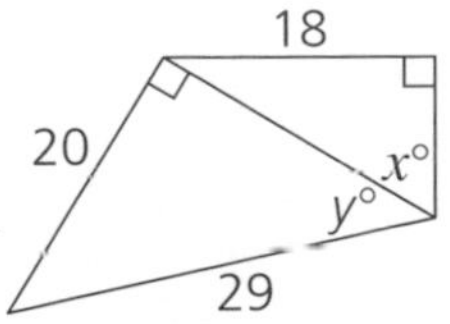

Show that the exact value of $\sin(x + y)°$ is $\frac{378 + 60\sqrt{13}}{609}$

2. d.

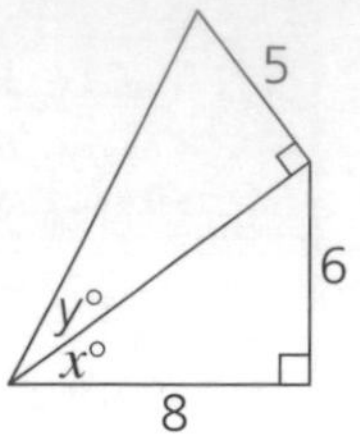

Show that $\cos (x + y)° = \frac{1}{\sqrt{5}}$

e.

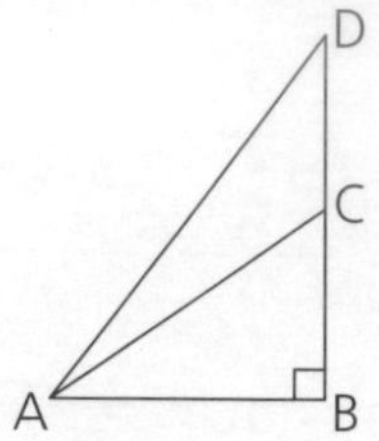

AB = 9 cm, AC = 11 cm and BD = 12 cm.

If $\angle BAD = x°$ and $\angle BAC = y°$ then show that

$\sin (x - y)° = \frac{108 - 18\sqrt{10}}{165}$

See these pages in Leckie & Leckie's *Higher Maths Course Notes:*

page 35, example 10.5 (1st ed: page 35, example 10.4)

Exercise 10.8 Exact values and Double Angle Formula

1. In each case $0 < \alpha < \frac{\pi}{2}$. Draw a right-angled triangle to find the required exact value.

a. $\sin \alpha = \frac{1}{\sqrt{5}}$. Find $\cos \alpha$

b. $\tan \alpha = \frac{\sqrt{3}}{4}$. Find $\sin \alpha$

c. $\cos \alpha = \frac{1}{8}$. Find $\tan \alpha$

d. $\sin \alpha = \frac{\sqrt{3}}{\sqrt{5}}$. Find $\tan \alpha$

e. $\tan \alpha = \frac{\sqrt{7}}{\sqrt{3}}$. Find $\cos \alpha$

2. If $0 < \alpha < \frac{\pi}{2}$ find the exact value of $\sin 2\alpha$ given that:

a. $\tan \alpha = \frac{1}{3}$ **b.** $\cos \alpha = \frac{2}{\sqrt{7}}$ **c.** $\sin \alpha = \frac{\sqrt{2}}{5}$ **d.** $\cos \alpha = \frac{\sqrt{3}}{\sqrt{5}}$

page 36, example 10.6 (1st ed: page 36, example 10.5)

Exercise 10.9 Double Angle Formulae varieties

Use the Double Angle Formula to rewrite:

1. $\sin 2B°$ **2.** $\sin \theta$ **3.** $\sin \alpha$

4. $\sin 4x°$ **5.** $\sin D°$ **6.** $\sin 3x°$

7. $\sin \left(\frac{x}{2}\right)°$ **8.** $\sin \left(\frac{2x}{3}\right)°$ **9.** $\sin \frac{\pi}{3}$

page 35. Read the discussion at the bottom of the page.

Exercise 10.10 Identities

Show that:

1. $(\cos x - \sin x)^2 = 1 - \sin 2x$

2. $(\cos \theta + \sin \theta)(\cos \theta - \sin \theta) = \cos 2\theta$

3. $(2\cos t - 1)(2\cos t + 1) = 2\cos 2t + 1$

4. $\frac{\sin 2x}{1 + \cos 2x} = \tan x$

5. $\frac{1 - \cos 2\phi}{1 + \cos 2\phi} = \tan^2 \phi$

page 36, example 10.7 (1st ed: page 36, example 10.6)

To pull out this section, remove the centre staple.

Pull-out answer section for Leckie & Leckie's QUESTIONS IN HIGHER MATHS

UNIT 1 1. THE STRAIGHT LINE

Exercise 1.1

1. 1 **2.** 3 **3.** –3
4. $\frac{1}{2}$ **5.** –5 **6.** $-\frac{1}{2}$
7. 0 **8.** $\frac{1}{4}$

Exercise 1.2

1. 45° **2.** 71·6° **3.** 108·4°
4. 26·6° **5.** 101·3° **6.** 153·4°
7. 0° **8.** 14·0°

Exercise 1.3

1. a. no **b.** yes **c.** yes
d. no **e.** yes

2. A_2

Exercise 1.4

1. a. $m_{AB} \times m_{BC} = \frac{2}{3} \times (-\frac{3}{2}) = -1$
b. $m_{AB} \times m_{BC} = -2 \times \frac{1}{2} = -1$

2. a. $m_{RP} \times m_{PQ} = -5 \times \frac{1}{5} = -1$; $\angle P$
b. $m_{DE} \times m_{EC} = -\frac{2}{5} \times \frac{5}{2} = -1$; $\angle E$
c. $m_{VU} \times m_{UW} = -\frac{7}{2} \times \frac{2}{7} = -1$; $\angle U$
d. $m_{CA} \times m_{AB} = -2 \times \frac{1}{2} = -1$; $\angle A$

Exercise 1.5

1. a. $-\frac{4}{3}$ **b.** $\frac{3}{2}$ **c.** $-\frac{1}{5}$
d. $\frac{1}{2}$ **e.** none **f.** –3
g. 2 **h.** $\frac{2}{5}$ **i.** $-\frac{2}{3}$

2. a. $-\frac{2}{3}$ **b.** $-\frac{2}{5}$ **c.** 2
d. $\frac{2}{3}$

Exercise 1.6

1. yes **2.** no **3.** yes
4. no **5.** yes **6.** yes

Exercise 1.7

1. $y - 2x = -1$ **2.** $2y - x = -7$
3. $2y + x = 8$ **4.** $y + 3x = 14$
5. $y + x = 4$ **6.** $4y - 2x = -3$

Exercise 1.8

1. (–2, 0), (0, 6) **2.** (–2, 0), (0, 3)
3. (6, 0), (0, 2) **4.** (–2, 0), (0, 5)
5. $(-\frac{5}{2}, 0), (0, 1)$ **6.** $(-\frac{5}{2}, 0), (0, -\frac{5}{3})$

Exercise 1.9

1. a. (2, 5) **b.** (–1, 3) **c.** (4, –2)
d. $(\frac{1}{2}, 0)$ **e.** (–2, –4) **f.** $(\frac{1}{2}, -\frac{3}{2})$

2. a. yes at (1, 5) **b.** no
c. no **d.** yes at $(\frac{1}{2}, 1)$

Exercise 1.10

1. 5 **2.** 10 **3.** 5
4. 13 **5.** $\sqrt{2}$ **6.** $\sqrt{20}$ or $2\sqrt{5}$
7. $\sqrt{68}$ or $2\sqrt{17}$ **8.** $\frac{\sqrt{2}}{2}$ (from $\frac{1}{\sqrt{2}}$)

Exercise 1.11

1. (6, 2) **2.** (1, 4) **3.** (–2, –1)
4. (–6, –2) **5.** $(\frac{5}{2}, \frac{3}{2})$ **6.** (1, –1)
7. $(-1, \frac{7}{2})$ **8.** $(-\frac{1}{2}, -\frac{3}{2})$

Exercise 1.12

1. $3y + 2x = 14$ **2.** $y = x + 2$
3. $y = -2x + 2$ **4.** $y = 3x + 20$
5. $y = -2x + 1$ **6.** $3y - x = 16$
7. $2y - 4x = 11$ **8.** $2y - 8x = 39$

Exercise 1.13

1. a. CD: $3y + x = 8$; AE: $2y - x = 2$; G(2, 2)
b. RS: $y + 2x = 6$; QT: $3y - 2x = 2$; G(2, 2)

2. a. BD: $2y - x = 0$; CE: $y + x = -3$
b. M(–2, –1)

3. G(0, –1)

4. concurrent at (3, –1)

3. FUNCTIONS AND GRAPHS

Exercise 3.1

All the real numbers apart from:
1. 0 **2.** –2 **3.** 4
4. 1 and –1 **5.** 2 and –2 **6.** 4 and –4
7. 0 **8.** $\frac{3}{2}$ and $-\frac{3}{2}$

All the real numbers x such that:
9. $x \geq 4$ **10.** $x \geq -3$
11. $x \leq 10$ **12.** $x \leq \frac{5}{2}$

Exercise 3.2

1. 9 **2.** −2 **3.** −28

4. $-\frac{1}{4}$ **5.** 4 **6.** 19

Exercise 3.3

1. a. move graph left 2 units
A′(−3, 2), B′(−1, 1), C′(0, 0)
b. move graph right 1 unit
A′(0, 2), B′(2, 1), C′(3, 0)
c. 'flip' the graph in the x-axis
A′(−1, −2), B′(1, −1), C′(2, 0)
d. move the graph down 1 unit
A′(−1, 1), B′(1, 0), C′(2, −1)

2. a. move graph right 2 units
A′(1, 0), B′(2, −1), C′(3, 0)
b. move graph left 1 unit
A′(−2, 0), B′(−1, −1), C′(0, 0)
c. 'flip' the graph in the x-axis
A′(−1, 0), B′(0, 1), C′(1, 0)
d. move the graph up 1 unit
A′(−1, 1), B′(0, 0), C′(1, 1)

3. a. move graph left 3 units
A′(−4, 0), B′(−3, 1), C′(−2, 0), D′(−1, −1), E′(0, 0)
b. move graph right 1 unit
A′(0, 0), B′(1, 1), C′(2, 0), D′(3, −1), E′(4, 0)
c. 'flip' the graph in the x-axis
A′(−1, 0), B′(0, −1), C′(1, 0), D′(2, 1), E′(3, 0)
d. move graph down 1 unit
A′(−1, −1), B′(0, 0), C′(1, −1), D′(2, −2), E′(3, −1)

4. a.

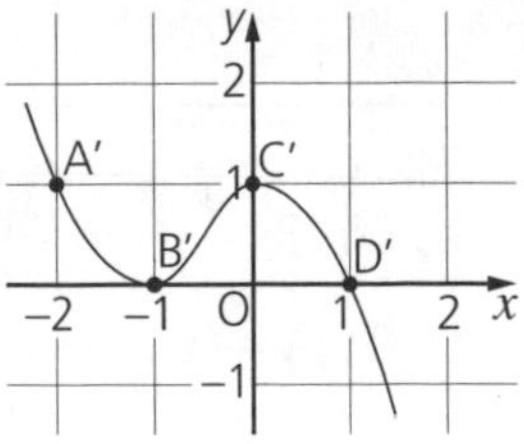

b.

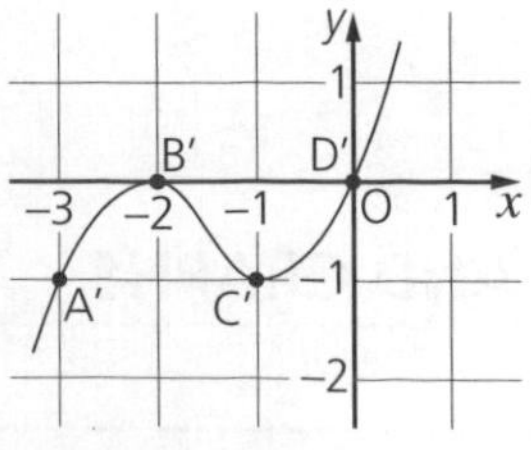

5. a.

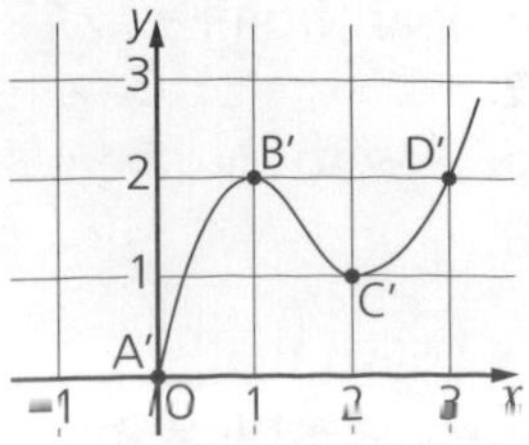

5. b.

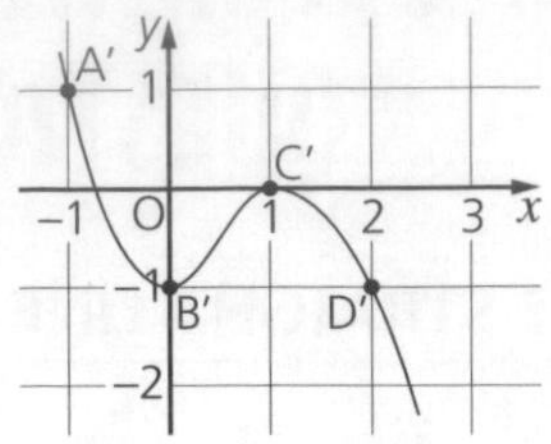

6. a.

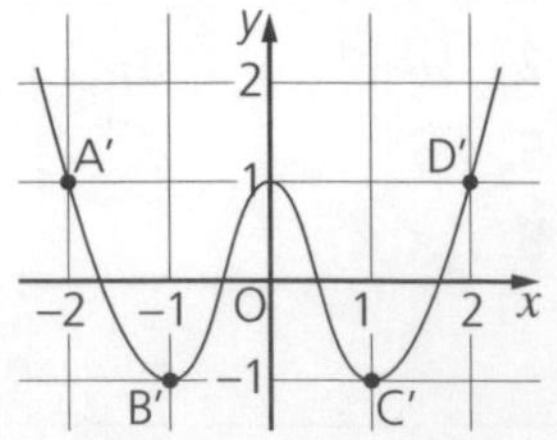

b.

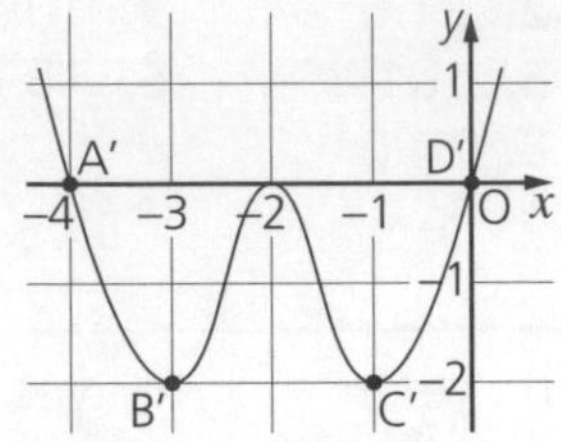

Exercise 3.4

1. a. $4x^2 - 1$ **b.** $8x - 1$
c. $4x + 3$ **d.** $11 - 4x$

2. a. $4x^2 + 2$ **b.** $x^2 - 2x + 3$
c. $9x^2 + 6x + 3$ **d.** $6 - 20x + 25x^2$

3. a. $9x^2 - 6x + 1$ **b.** $3x^2 - 1$
c. $9x - 4$ **d.** x^4

4. a. (i) $6x + 1$ **(ii)** $6x + 3$
b. (i) $2x^2$ **(ii)** $4x^2$
c. (i) $x^2 - 10x + 25$ **(ii)** $x^2 - 5$
d. (i) $4x^2 + 4x - 1$ **(ii)** $2x^2 - 3$

5. a. $2 - 2x - k$ **b.** $4 - 2x + k$
c. Proof **d.** $2k + 2$

6. a. Proof **b.** Proof

Exercise 3.5

1. a. $\frac{2-x}{x}$ **b.** $\frac{x-4}{x}$ **c.** $\frac{x+1}{x-1}$
d. $\frac{3-x}{x-1}$ **e.** $\frac{x+5}{x+1}$ **f.** $\frac{x-4}{x-1}$
g. $\frac{x^2-5}{x^2-9}$ **h.** $\frac{4-x^2}{x^2-1}$

2. a. $\frac{2-x}{x}$ **b.** $\frac{x+4}{x+1}$ **c.** $\frac{x-3}{x-1}$
d. $\frac{x^2+1}{x^2-1}$ **e.** $\frac{12-x^2}{x^2-9}$ **f.** $\frac{x^2+1}{x^2-1}$

Exercise 3.6

1. a.

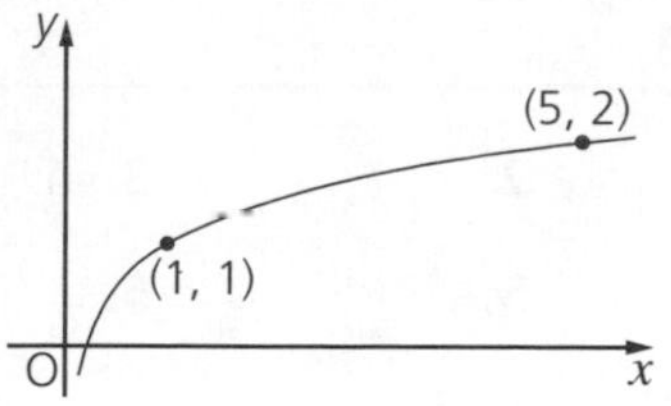

b.

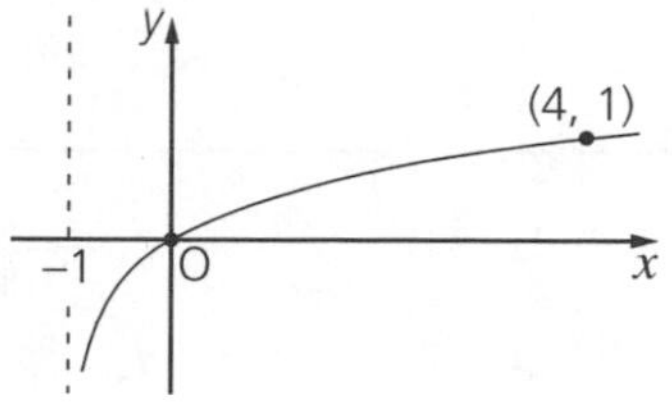

c.

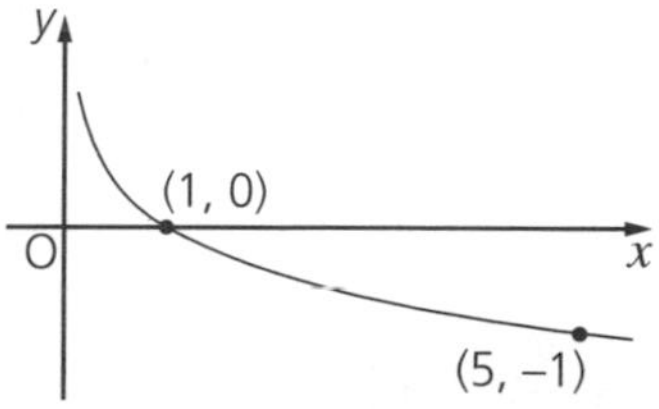

d.

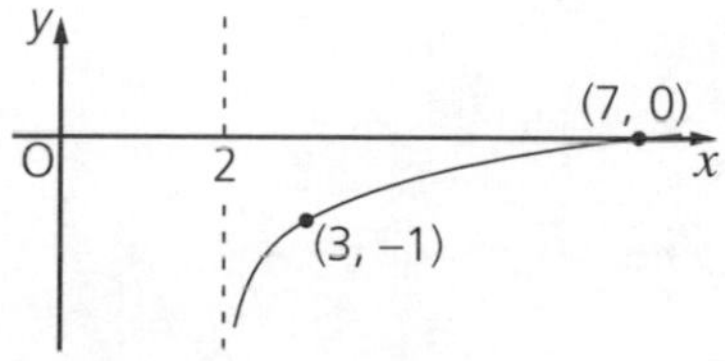

2. a.

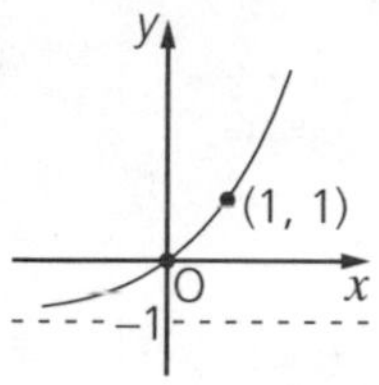

b.

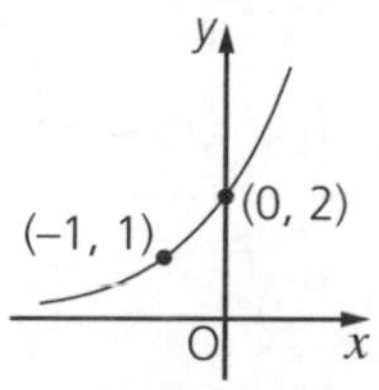

c.

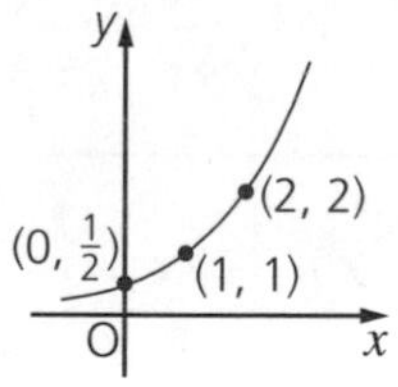

d.

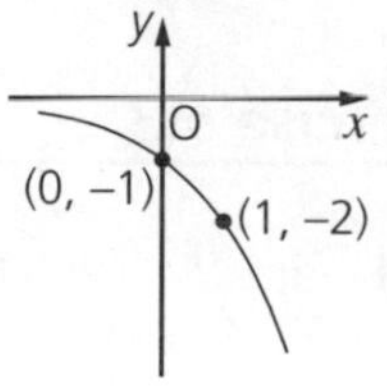

Exercise 3.7

1. a. $(x+2)^2-1$ **b.** $(x-3)^2-10$
c. $(x+\frac{3}{2})^2-\frac{5}{4}$ **d.** $(x+\frac{5}{2})^2-\frac{17}{4}$
e. $(x-\frac{5}{2})^2-\frac{17}{4}$ **f.** $(x-\frac{1}{2})^2-\frac{17}{4}$
g. $(x+\frac{1}{2})^2-\frac{29}{4}$ **h.** $(x+\frac{5}{2})^2-\frac{25}{4}$

2. a. $2(x^2-2x+\frac{1}{2})$ **b.** $3(x^2+2x+\frac{2}{3})$
c. $5(x^2+3x-\frac{7}{5})$ **d.** $2(x^2-5x-\frac{5}{2})$
e. $4(x^2+3x+\frac{17}{4})$ **f.** $7(x^2-4x-\frac{12}{7})$
g. $2(x^2+\frac{3}{2}x-\frac{1}{2})$ **h.** $3(x^2+\frac{5}{3}x+\frac{7}{3})$

3. a. $2(x+1)^2-1$ **b.** $3(x-1)^2-5$
c. $4(x+2)^2-1$ **d.** $4(x-1)^2-1$
e. $9(x+1)^2-1$ **f.** $25(x+1)^2-36$
g. $2(x+\frac{3}{4})^2-\frac{25}{8}$ **h.** $5(x-\frac{1}{2})^2+\frac{27}{4}$

4. TRIGONOMETRY – BASIC FACTS

Exercise 4.1

1. $x = 0, 180, 360$ **2.** $x = 0$
3. $x = 180$ **4.** $x = 90$
5. $x = 0, 360$ **6.** $x = 270$
7. $x = 270$ **8.** $x = 360$

Exercise 4.2

1. a. $\frac{1}{\sqrt{2}}$ **b.** $\frac{\sqrt{3}}{2}$ **c.** $\frac{1}{2}$
d. $\frac{1}{\sqrt{2}}$ **e.** 1 **f.** $\sqrt{3}$
g. $\frac{\sqrt{3}}{2}$ **h.** $\frac{1}{2}$ **i.** 1
j. $\frac{1}{\sqrt{2}}$ **k.** $\frac{\sqrt{3}}{2}$ **l.** $\frac{1}{\sqrt{3}}$

2. a. 60 **b.** $\frac{\pi}{3}$ **c.** $\frac{\pi}{3}$
d. 30 **e.** 30 **f.** 45
g. $\frac{\pi}{3}$ **h.** $\frac{\pi}{6}$

Exercise 4.3

1. a. Max: $(0, 1)$, $(2\pi, 1)$; Min: $(\pi, -1)$
b. Max: $(\frac{\pi}{2}, 3)$; Min: $(\frac{3\pi}{2}, -3)$
c. Max: $(0, 2)$, $(2\pi, 2)$; Min: $(\pi, -2)$
d. Max: $(\frac{\pi}{2}, \frac{1}{2})$; Min: $(\frac{3\pi}{2}, -\frac{1}{2})$
e. Max: $(\frac{\pi}{2}, 10)$; Min: $(\frac{3\pi}{2}, -10)$
f. Max: $(0, \frac{1}{2})$, $(2\pi, \frac{1}{2})$; Min: $(\pi, -\frac{1}{2})$
g. Max: $(\frac{3\pi}{2}, 1)$; Min: $(\frac{\pi}{2}, -1)$
h. Max: $(\pi, 1)$; Min: $(0, -1)$, $(2\pi, -1)$

2. a. $\frac{\pi}{6}$ **b.** $\frac{5\pi}{3}$ **c.** $\frac{7\pi}{4}$
d. $\frac{\pi}{3}$ **e.** $\frac{7\pi}{6}$ **f.** $\frac{3\pi}{4}$
g. $\frac{2\pi}{3}$ **h.** $\frac{11\pi}{6}$ **i.** $\frac{4\pi}{3}$

3. a. Max: $(\frac{11\pi}{6}, 2)$; Min: $(\frac{5\pi}{6}, -2)$

b. Max: $(\frac{\pi}{6}, 4)$; Min: $(\frac{7\pi}{6}, -4)$

c. Max: $(\frac{\pi}{4}, 5)$; Min: $(\frac{5\pi}{4}, -5)$

d. Max: $(\frac{2\pi}{3}, 2)$; Min: $(\frac{5\pi}{3}, -2)$

e. Max: $(\frac{3\pi}{4}, 15)$; Min: $(\frac{7\pi}{4}, -15)$

f. Max: $(\frac{5\pi}{3}, 6)$; Min: $(\frac{2\pi}{3}, -6)$

g. Max: $(\frac{\pi}{3}, 3)$; Min: $(\frac{4\pi}{3}, -3)$

h. Max: $(\frac{\pi}{5}, 10)$; Min: $(\frac{6\pi}{5}, -10)$

Exercise 4.4

1. a. $a = \frac{\pi}{6}$ **b.** $a = \frac{\pi}{3}$

2. a. $a = 4, b = 2$ **b.** $a = 5, b = 3$

Exercise 4.5

1.

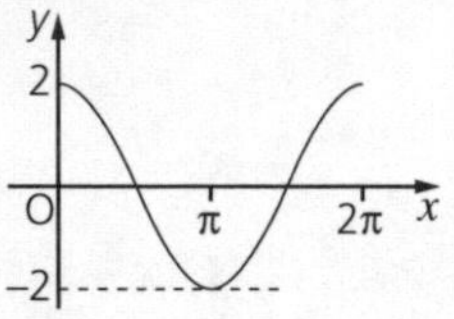

2.

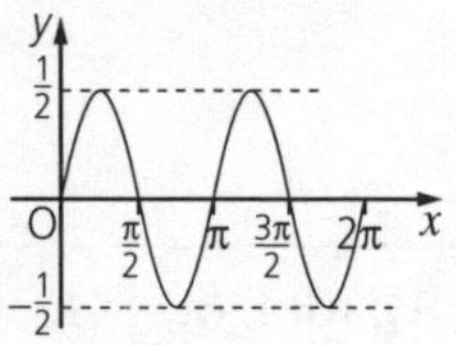

3.

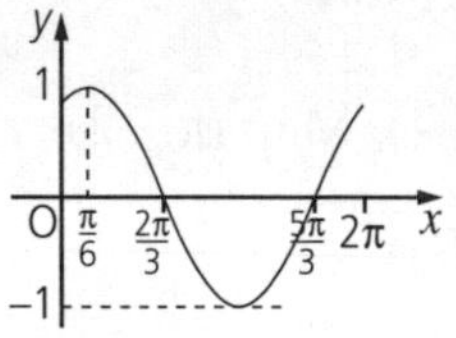

4.

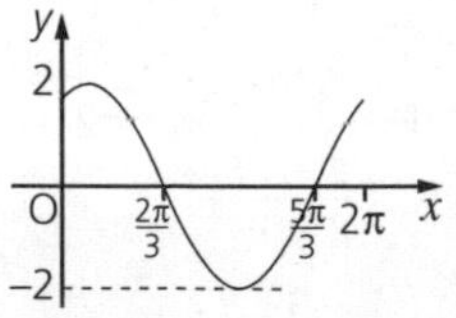

5.

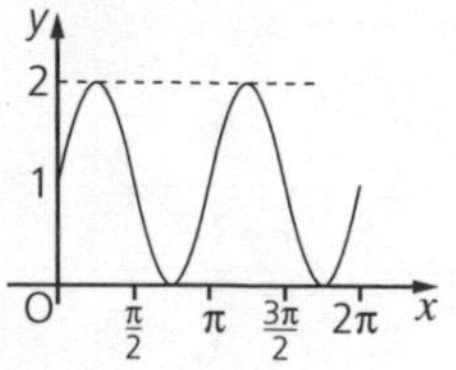

6.

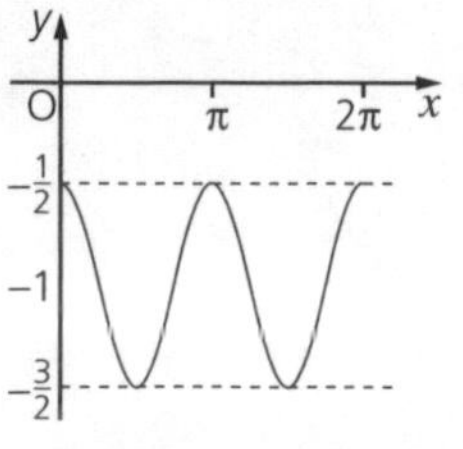

5. INTRODUCTION TO DIFFERENTIATION

Exercise 5.1

1. $-\frac{3}{4}$ **2.** 1 **3.** 4

4. $-\frac{1}{2}$ **5.** $\frac{1}{3}$ **6.** $\frac{5}{3}$

7. $-\frac{2}{3}$ **8.** 0

Exercise 5.2

1. a. $-\frac{8}{x^5}$ **b.** $\frac{6}{x^3}$ **c.** $-\frac{5}{x^6}$

d. $-\frac{5}{x^2}$ **e.** $\frac{4}{x^2}$ **f.** $\frac{3}{x^4}$

g. $-\frac{1}{x^{\frac{3}{2}}} = -\frac{1}{(\sqrt{x})^3}$ **h.** $\frac{1}{2x^{\frac{3}{2}}} = \frac{1}{2(\sqrt{x})^3}$

2. a. $f'(x) = \frac{1}{2}x^{-\frac{1}{2}} + \frac{3}{2}x^{\frac{1}{2}}$

b. $\frac{dy}{dx} = -x^{-\frac{1}{2}} + \frac{1}{2}x^{-\frac{3}{2}}$

c. $\frac{dy}{dx} = -\frac{5}{2}x^{-\frac{3}{2}} - 2x^{-2}$

d. $f'(x) = -6x^{-3} - \frac{1}{2}x^{-2}$

e. $\frac{dy}{dx} = \frac{1}{3}x^{-\frac{1}{2}} + x^{-\frac{3}{2}}$

f. $f'(x) = -3x^{-4} + 2x^{-3} + x^{-2}$

g. $f'(x) = \frac{1}{2}x^{\frac{1}{2}} + \frac{1}{3}x^{-\frac{3}{2}}$

h. $f'(x) = \frac{3}{2}x^{-\frac{5}{2}} + \frac{3}{2}x^{-\frac{3}{2}}$

Exercise 5.3

1. a. $\frac{1}{2\sqrt{x}}$ **b.** $\frac{5}{2}(\sqrt{x})^3$ **c.** $\frac{3}{2}\sqrt{x}$

d. $\frac{1}{2\sqrt{x}}$ **e.** $-\frac{1}{2(\sqrt{x})^3}$ **f.** $\frac{7}{2}(\sqrt{x})^5$

g. $-\frac{3}{2(\sqrt{x})^5}$ **h.** $\frac{3}{2}\sqrt{x}$

2. a. $-\frac{12}{x^4} + \frac{1}{2\sqrt{x}}$ **b.** $\frac{3}{x^2} - \frac{3}{2}\sqrt{x}$

c. $-\frac{1}{x^2} - \frac{1}{2\sqrt{x}}$ **d.** $\frac{15}{x^4} - \frac{5}{2}(\sqrt{x})^3$

e. $\frac{3}{2}\sqrt{x} - \frac{8}{x^2}$ **f.** $-\frac{1}{2(\sqrt{x})^3} + \frac{6}{x^3}$

g. $\frac{3}{2}\sqrt{x} + \frac{3}{2(\sqrt{x})^5}$ **h.** $3\sqrt{x} - \frac{3}{2(\sqrt{x})^5}$

3. a. $-\frac{1}{x^2}$ **b.** $-\frac{3}{2(\sqrt{x})^3}$

c. $-\frac{1}{(\sqrt{x})^3}$ **d.** $-\frac{2}{x^3} - \frac{1}{2\sqrt{x}}$

e. $\frac{3}{2\sqrt{x}} + \frac{2}{x^2}$ **f.** $\frac{1}{\sqrt{x}} - \frac{1}{2(\sqrt{x})^3}$

3. **g.** $-\frac{1}{2(\sqrt{x})^3} - \frac{3}{2}\sqrt{x}$ **h.** $-\frac{6}{x^3} + \frac{2}{x^2}$

i. $-\frac{1}{2(\sqrt{x})^3} - \frac{1}{\sqrt{x}}$ **j.** $\frac{1}{2\sqrt{x}} - \frac{1}{2(\sqrt{x})^3}$

k. $\frac{1}{2\sqrt{x}}$ **l.** $-\frac{1}{x^2} + \frac{1}{2(\sqrt{x})^3}$

m. $-\frac{1}{2(\sqrt{x})^3} + 3\sqrt{x}$ **n.** $2x + \frac{1}{(\sqrt{x})^3}$

o. $-\frac{1}{2(\sqrt{x})^3} - 1$ **p.** $\frac{1}{6\sqrt{x}} - \frac{1}{6(\sqrt{x})^3}$

Exercise 5.4

1. $\frac{1}{4}$ **2.** -24 **3.** $\frac{1}{2}$
4. $\frac{13}{3}$ **5.** $-\frac{1}{2}$ **6.** $-\frac{5}{16}$
7. $\frac{163}{6}$ **8.** $-\frac{5}{12}$

Exercise 5.5

1.
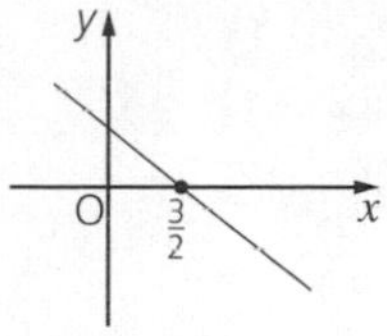

2.
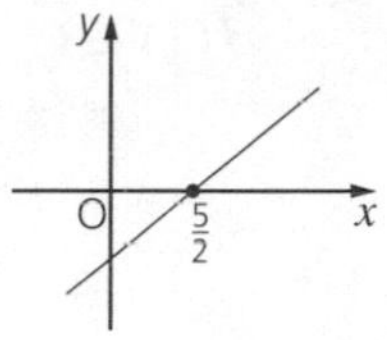

3.
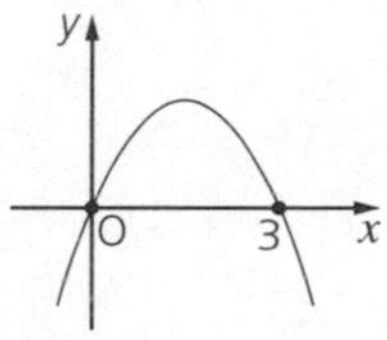

4.
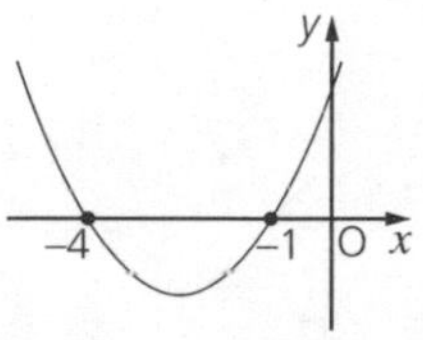

5.
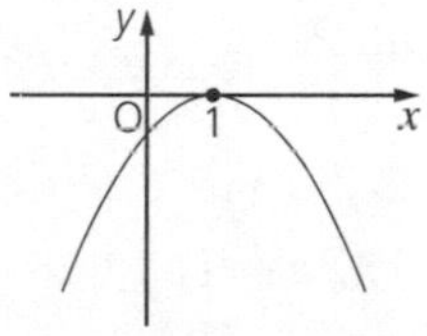

6.
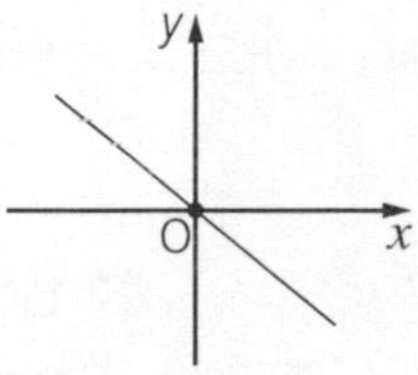

7.
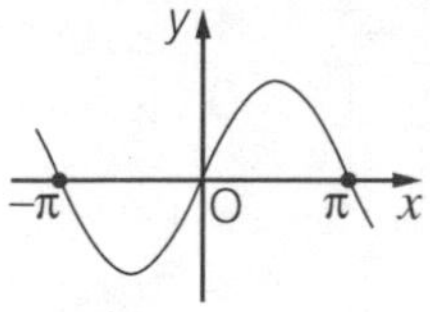

8.
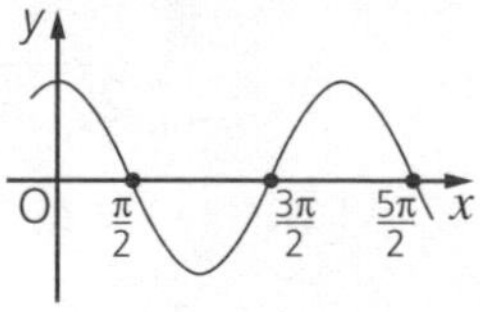

Exercise 5.6

1. Increasing (3) **2.** Increasing (6)
3. Increasing (1) **4.** Stationary (0)
5. Decreasing (–6) **6.** Stationary (0)
7. Decreasing (–7) **8.** Increasing (13)

Exercise 5.7

1. (2, 7) and (–2, –1) **2.** $(-\frac{2}{3}, -\frac{28}{27})$ and (1, 1)
3. $(3, -\frac{2}{3})$ and $(-3, \frac{2}{3})$ **4.** $(\frac{9}{4}, \frac{3}{2})$

Exercise 5.8

1. **a.** $y = -7x - 4$ **b.** $y = 7x - 8$
c. $y = -2x + 7$ **d.** $y = 7x + 22$

2. **a.** tangents at A and C
b. at A: $3y + 3x = 5$ at B: $y = -2x + 1$
at C: $3y + 3x = 1$

Exercise 5.9

1. (0, 2), (6, –106); Max, Min
2. (–3, –28), (0, –1); Min, Rising point of inflexion (POI)
3. (–2, 22), (1, –5); Max, Min
4. (0, 0), (1, 1); Min, Rising POI
5. (–1, –1), (0, –2); Max, Min
6. (–2, –59), (0, 5), (3, –184); Min, Max, Min
7. (0, 0), (2, 16); Both rising POIs
8. $(-\frac{1}{2}, 1)$, $(0, \frac{7}{8})$; Falling POI, Min

Exercise 5.10

1. $0 < x < 4$ **2.** $-1 < x < 3$
3. $x < 1$ or $x > 5$ **4.** $x < -4$ or $x > 1$
5. $-1 \le x \le -\frac{1}{3}$ **6.** $-\frac{1}{3} \le x \le \frac{4}{3}$
7. $x < \frac{1}{2}$ or $x > \frac{4}{3}$ **8.** $x \le -\frac{4}{3}$ or $x \ge \frac{2}{5}$

Exercise 5.11

1. stone 1: **a.** 60 m/s **b.** 40 m/s **c.** 20 m/s
stone 2: **a.** 56 m/s **b.** 28 m/s **c.** 0 m/s
stone 3: **a.** 16 m/s **b.** 0 m/s **c.** –16 m/s

2. **a.** 400 m/min **b.** 0 m/min (maximum height) **c.** –400 m/min (lands)

6. RECURRENCE RELATIONS

Exercise 6.1

1. **a.** 32 **b.** 16 **c.** 0
d. 22 **e.** 27 **f.** 95
g. 11 **h.** 33 **i.** 64

2. **a.** 16 **b.** 9 **c.** –12
d. 16 **e.** 41 **f.** 42

Exercise 6.2

1. –1 < multiplier (0·8) < 1 so a limit exists
2. multiplier (1·1) > 1 so there is no limit
3. multiplier (2) > 1 so there is no limit
4. –1 < multiplier $(-\frac{1}{2})$ < 1 so a limit exists
5. multiplier $(\frac{3}{2})$ > 1 so there is no limit
6. –1 < multiplier $(\frac{1}{3})$ < 1 so a limit exists
7. –1 < multiplier $(\frac{2}{3})$ < 1 so a limit exists
8. multiplier $(\frac{3}{2})$ > 1 so there is no limit

Exercise 6.3

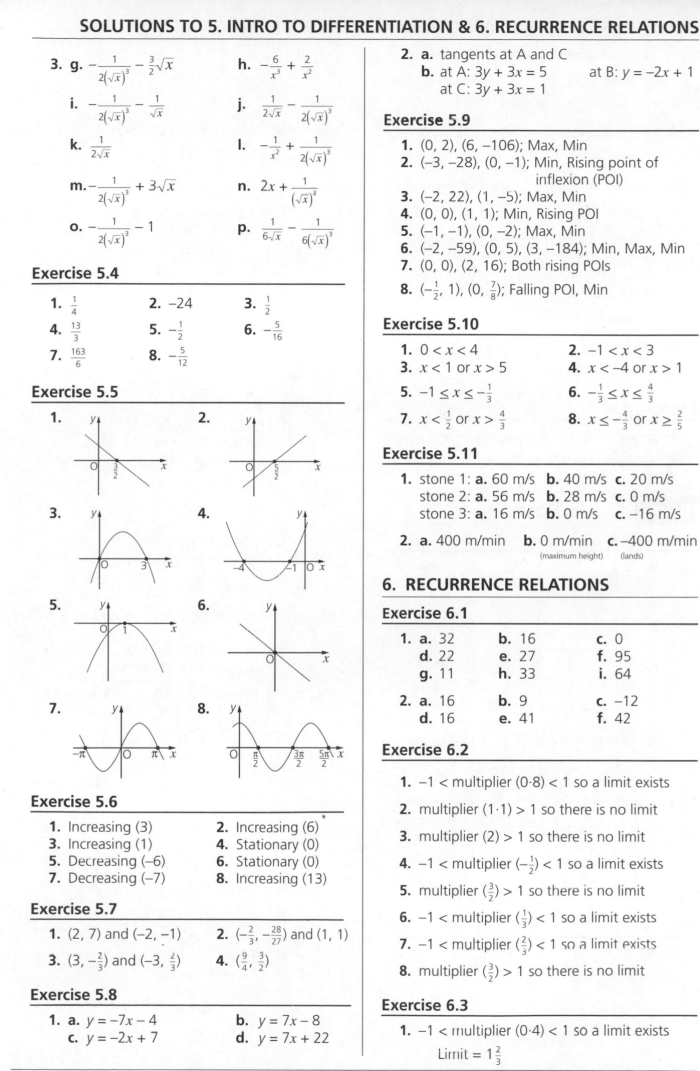

1. –1 < multiplier (0·4) < 1 so a limit exists
Limit = $1\frac{2}{3}$

2. $-1 <$ multiplier $(0{\cdot}7) < 1$ so a limit exists

Limit $= 26\frac{2}{3}$

3. multiplier $(\frac{3}{2}) > 1$ so there is no limit

4. $-1 <$ multiplier $(\frac{1}{4}) < 1$ so a limit exists

Limit $= 6\frac{2}{3}$

5. $-1 <$ multiplier $(\frac{2}{7}) < 1$ so a limit exists

Limit $= 1\frac{3}{5}$ $(= 1{\cdot}6)$

6. $-1 <$ multiplier $(\frac{1}{3}) < 1$ so a limit exists

Limit $= -\frac{3}{2}$ $(= -1{\cdot}5)$

7. $-1 <$ multiplier $(\frac{4}{11}) < 1$ so a limit exists

Limit $= 1\frac{4}{7}$

8. $-1 <$ multiplier $(\frac{14}{23}) < 1$ so a limit exists

Limit $= 5\frac{1}{9}$

Exercise 6.4

1. 60 kg **2.** $16\frac{2}{3}$ litres **3.** 1000 ants

4. a. Yes (limit is 40) **b.** No (limit is $51\frac{3}{7}$)

5. No (limit is 75)

UNIT 2 7. POLYNOMIALS

Exercise 7.1

1. a.
$$\begin{array}{r|rrrr} -1 & 1 & -6 & 3 & 10 \\ & & -1 & 7 & -10 \\ \hline & 1 & -7 & 10 & 0 \end{array}$$
Remainder is zero so $x + 1$ is a factor

b.
$$\begin{array}{r|rrrr} 2 & 1 & -1 & 1 & -6 \\ & & 2 & 2 & 6 \\ \hline & 1 & 1 & 3 & 0 \end{array}$$
Remainder is zero so $x - 2$ is a factor

c.
$$\begin{array}{r|rrrr} -4 & 4 & 16 & -1 & -4 \\ & & -16 & 0 & 4 \\ \hline & 4 & 0 & -1 & 0 \end{array}$$
Remainder is zero so $x + 4$ is a factor

d.
$$\begin{array}{r|rrrr} 1 & 1 & 0 & -7 & 6 \\ & & 1 & 1 & -6 \\ \hline & 1 & 1 & -6 & 0 \end{array}$$
Remainder is zero so $x - 1$ is a factor

2.
$$\begin{array}{r|rrrrr} -2 & 1 & 0 & -15 & -10 & 24 \\ & & -2 & 4 & 22 & -24 \\ \hline & 1 & -2 & -11 & 12 & 0 \end{array}$$
Remainder is zero so $x + 2$ is a factor

$$\begin{array}{r|rrrrr} 4 & 1 & 0 & -15 & -10 & 24 \\ & & 4 & 16 & 4 & -24 \\ \hline & 1 & 4 & 1 & -6 & 0 \end{array}$$
Remainder is zero so $x - 4$ is a factor

Exercise 7.2

1. a.
$$\begin{array}{r|rrrr} 3 & 1 & -1 & -5 & -3 \\ & & 3 & 6 & 3 \\ \hline & 1 & 2 & 1 & 0 \end{array}$$
$$\begin{aligned} f(x) &= (x-3)(x^2+2x+1) \\ &= (x-3)(x+1)(x+1) \\ &= (x-3)(x+1)^2 \end{aligned}$$

1. b.
$$\begin{array}{r|rrrr} 1 & 1 & -6 & 11 & -6 \\ & & 1 & -5 & 6 \\ \hline & 1 & -5 & 6 & 0 \end{array}$$
$$\begin{aligned} f(x) &= (x-1)(x^2-5x+6) \\ &= (x-1)(x-2)(x-3) \end{aligned}$$

c.
$$\begin{array}{r|rrrr} 2 & 1 & 0 & -7 & 6 \\ & & 2 & 4 & -6 \\ \hline & 1 & 2 & -3 & 0 \end{array}$$
$$\begin{aligned} f(x) &= (x-2)(x^2+2x-3) \\ &= (x-2)(x+3)(x-1) \end{aligned}$$

d.
$$\begin{array}{r|rrrr} 1 & 6 & -5 & -2 & 1 \\ & & 6 & 1 & -1 \\ \hline & 6 & 1 & -1 & 0 \end{array}$$
$$\begin{aligned} f(x) &= (x-1)(6x^2+x-1) \\ &= (x-1)(2x+1)(3x-1) \end{aligned}$$

e.
$$\begin{array}{r|rrrr} -2 & 1 & 0 & -3 & 2 \\ & & -2 & 4 & -2 \\ \hline & 1 & -2 & 1 & 0 \end{array}$$
$$\begin{aligned} f(x) &= (x+2)(x^2-2x+1) \\ &= (x+2)(x-1)(x-1) \\ &= (x+2)(x-1)^2 \end{aligned}$$

f.
$$\begin{array}{r|rrrr} -1 & 4 & 4 & -1 & -1 \\ & & -4 & 0 & 1 \\ \hline & 4 & 0 & -1 & 0 \end{array}$$
$$\begin{aligned} f(x) &= (x+1)(4x^2-1) \\ &= (x+1)(2x-1)(2x+1) \end{aligned}$$

g.
$$\begin{array}{r|rrrr} -3 & 2 & 7 & 2 & -3 \\ & & -6 & -3 & 3 \\ \hline & 2 & 1 & -1 & 0 \end{array}$$
$$\begin{aligned} f(x) &= (x+3)(2x^2+x-1) \\ &= (x+3)(x+1)(2x-1) \end{aligned}$$

2. a.
$$\begin{array}{r|rrrrr} 1 & 2 & -3 & -1 & 3 & -1 \\ & & 2 & -1 & -2 & 1 \\ \hline & 2 & -1 & -2 & 1 & 0 \end{array}$$
Remainder is zero so $x - 1$ is a factor

b. $f(x) = (x-1)(2x^3 - x^2 - 2x + 1)$

c.
$$\begin{array}{r|rrrr} -1 & 2 & -1 & -2 & 1 \\ & & -2 & 3 & -1 \\ \hline & 2 & -3 & 1 & 0 \end{array}$$
Remainder is zero so $x + 1$ is a factor

d.
$$\begin{aligned} f(x) &= (x-1)(x+1)(2x^2-3x+1) \\ &= (x-1)(x+1)(2x-1)(x-1) \end{aligned}$$

3. a. $(x-1)(2x-1)(2x+1)$
b. $(x+1)(x^2-x-1)$
c. $(x-2)(x-2)(x-2)$
d. $(x+2)(2x+1)(3x-1)$
e. $(x-3)(2x^2-3x-1)$
f. $(x+2)(2x^2-4x+5)$
g. $(x-2)(x^2+2x+4)$
h. $(x+3)(x^2-3x+9)$

Exercise 7.3

1. a. $x = -1, 0$ b. $y = -3, 1, 2$
 c. $x = -\frac{1}{2}, 2, 3$ d. $t = -1, 0, 1$
 e. $x = -\frac{1}{2}, \frac{2}{3}, 1$ f. $y = -\frac{1}{2}, \frac{1}{2}, 3$
 g. $x = -3, 0$
2. a. (1, 5), (2, 7) b. (–2, –7), (–1, –4), (2, 5)
 c. (–3, 16), (2, 6) d. (–3, –1), (–2, 0), (3, 5)
3. D(1, –3)

8. QUADRATIC THEORY

Exercise 8.1

1.
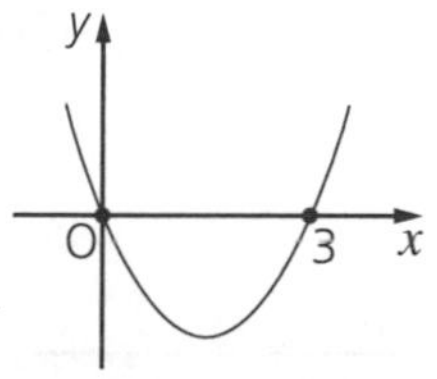

2.
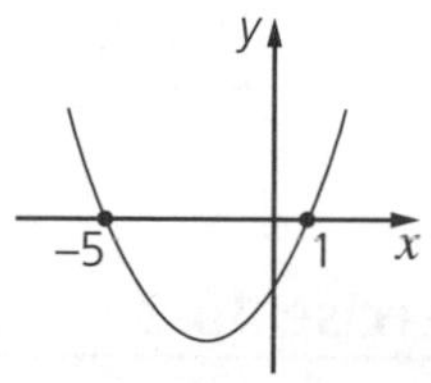

3.
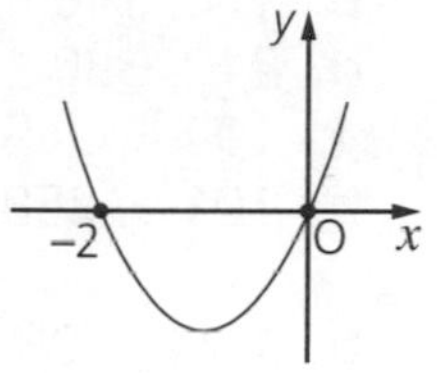

4.
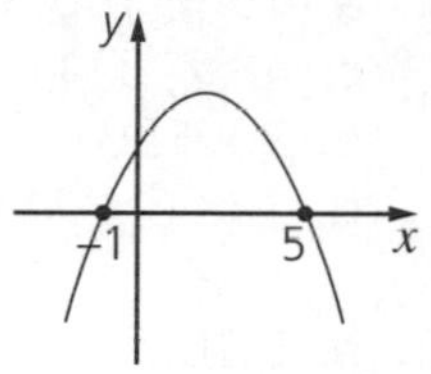

5.
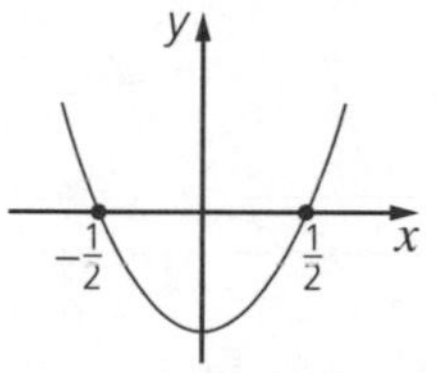

6.
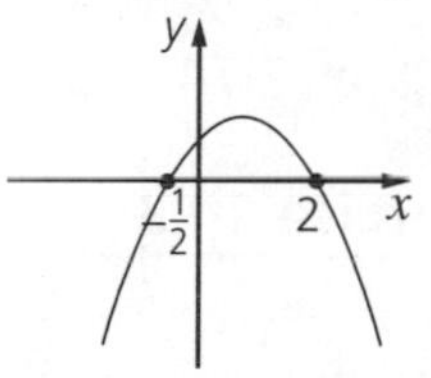

7.
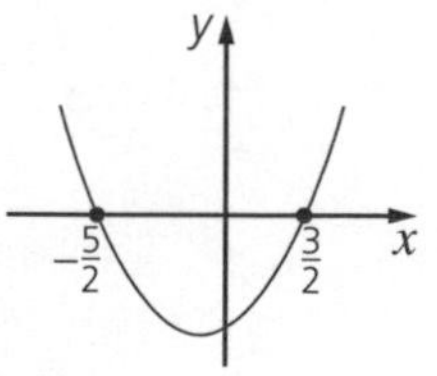

8.
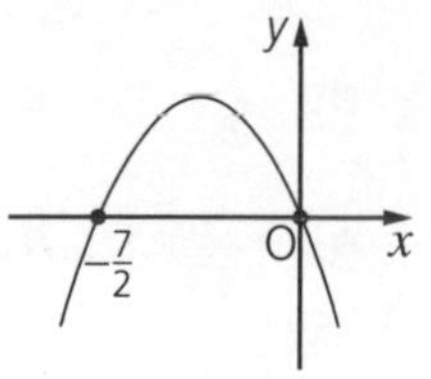

Exercise 8.2

1. –7; no real roots
2. 9; two distinct roots
3. 0; equal roots (one root only)
4. 0; equal roots (one root only)
5. –23; no real roots
6. 21; two distinct roots
7. 0; equal roots (one root only)
8. 245; two distinct roots

Exercise 8.3

1. a. yes (0) b. yes (0) c. no (4)
 d. yes (0) e. no (72) f. no (16)
 g. yes (0) h. yes (0)
2. a. $4x^2 + 12x + 9 = 0 \Rightarrow$ Discriminant = 0
 b. $x^2 - 14x + 49 = 0 \Rightarrow$ Discriminant = 0
 c. $25x^2 - 10x + 1 = 0 \Rightarrow$ Discriminant = 0
 In each case **a** – **c**, set formulae equal to each other.
 d. substitute $y = -2x + 5$
 $\Rightarrow 5x^2 - 20x + 20 = 0$
 $\Rightarrow$ Discriminant = 0
 e. substitute $x = -2y + 7$
 $\Rightarrow 5y^2 - 20y + 20 = 0$
 $\Rightarrow$ Discriminant = 0

Exercise 8.4

1. a. $a = 2$ b. $a = \frac{1}{4}$ c. $a = \frac{3}{4}$
 d. $c = \frac{1}{3}$ e. $c = 2$ f. $c = -3$
 g. $b = \pm 8$ h. $b = \pm 4$
2. a. 0, 8 b. –1 c. $-\frac{1}{2}, \frac{3}{2}$
 d. 4, –4 e. 0, –4 f. 2, –2
 g. 2 h. 5, –5
3. a. $k \leq 4$ b. $k > \frac{1}{3}$
 c. $k = \pm 4$ d. $-\frac{3}{2} \leq k \leq \frac{3}{2}$
 e. $k = -2, \frac{2}{3}$

Exercise 8.5

1. $-2 \leq x \leq 3$
2. $-5 < x < 2$
3. $x < -8$ or $x > 0$
4. $x \leq -3$ or $x \geq -1$
5. $-1 \leq x \leq 6$
6. $x \leq -3$ or $x \geq -2$
7. $-4 \leq x \leq 3$
8. $-4 < x < 5$
9. $x < -3$ or $x > 2$
10. $x \leq \frac{2}{3}$ or $x \geq \frac{3}{2}$

9. INTRODUCTION TO INTEGRATION

Exercise 9.1

1. a. $\frac{x^4}{4} + C$ b. $2x^2 + C$ c. $x^5 + C$
 d. $2x^3 + C$ e. $\frac{x^3}{3} + C$ f. $-x^3 + C$
 g. $-2x^5 + C$ h. $\frac{5x^3}{3} + C$
2. a. $-\frac{1}{x} + C$ b. $-\frac{5}{2x^2} + C$ c. $\frac{3}{x} + C$
 d. $-\frac{5}{2x} + C$ e. $-\frac{1}{9x^3} + C$ f. $\frac{1}{5x^2} + C$
3. a. $\frac{x^2}{2} + \frac{2}{x} + C$ b. $-\frac{1}{2x^2} - \frac{2x^3}{3} + C$
 c. $\frac{5x^2}{2} + \frac{1}{x^5} + C$ d. $-\frac{2}{x^2} - \frac{1}{x^3} + C$
 e. $-\frac{3}{2x} - \frac{1}{3x^5} + C$ f. $\frac{5x^3}{3} + 5x + \frac{3}{2x} + C$

Exercise 9.2

1. a. $\frac{2x^{\frac{3}{2}}}{3} + C$ **b.** $2x^{\frac{3}{2}} + C$

c. $4x^{\frac{1}{2}} + C$ **d.** $\frac{5x^{\frac{3}{2}}}{3} + C$

e. $x^{\frac{1}{2}} + C$ **f.** $\frac{2x^{\frac{1}{2}}}{3} + C$

2. a. $\frac{10(\sqrt{x})^3}{3} + C$

b. $8\sqrt{x} + C$

c. $\frac{x^2}{2} - 2\sqrt{x} + C$

d. $\frac{4\sqrt{x}}{3} + \frac{2(\sqrt{x})^3}{3} + C$

e. $4(\sqrt{x})^3 - 12\sqrt{x} + C$

f. $\frac{x^2}{2} - \frac{2(\sqrt{x})^5}{5} + C$

Exercise 9.3

1. 2 **2.** 3 **3.** –2

4. $\frac{39}{2}$ **5.** 26 **6.** $\frac{11}{6}$

Exercise 9.4

1. 4 **2.** 38 **3.** 6

4. $\frac{32}{3}$ **5.** $\frac{8}{3}$ **6.** $\frac{20}{3}$

7. $\frac{164}{9}$ **8.** $\frac{23}{8}$

Exercise 9.5

1. 4 unit² **2.** 4 unit² **3.** $\frac{32}{3}$ unit²

4. $\frac{9}{2}$ unit²

Exercise 9.6

1. a. 4 unit² **b.** 1 unit² **c.** 4 unit²

2. a. $\frac{9}{2}$ unit² **b.** $\frac{4}{3}$ unit² **c.** $\frac{1}{2}$ unit²

d. $\frac{4}{3}$ unit² **e.** $\frac{4}{3}$ unit² **f.** $\frac{125}{6}$ unit²

10. FURTHER TRIGONOMETRY

Exercise 10.1

1. a. 1st and 2nd **b.** 2nd and 4th
c. 2nd and 3rd **d.** 3rd and 4th
e. 1st and 4th **f.** 1st and 3rd
g. all four **h.** all four
i. all four

2. a. 19·5° **b.** 84·3° **c.** 48·2°
d. 56·3° **e.** 14·3° **f.** 61·9°

3. a. 0·201 **b.** 0·451 **c.** 0·951
d. 1·05 **e.** 1·11 **f.** 0·224

4. a. 210°, 330° **b.** 60°, 300°
c. 135°, 225° **d.** 156·4°, 336·4°
e. 80·1°, 99·9°, 260·1°, 279·9°
f. 192·9°, 347·1°

Exercise 10.2

1. a. 19·5, 160·5 **b.** 120, 240
c. 48·2, 311·8 **d.** 210, 330
e. 30, 150 **f.** 194·5, 345·5
g. 138·6, 221·4 **h.** 101·5, 258·5

2. a. 0·100, 3·04 **b.** 1·23, 5·05
c. 2·68, 5·82 **d.** 3·87, 5·55
e. 2·74, 3·54 **f.** 1·15, 4·29

Exercise 10.3

1. a. $\frac{1}{2}$ **b.** $\frac{\sqrt{3}}{2}$ **c.** $-\frac{1}{\sqrt{2}}$

d. $-\frac{1}{2}$ **e.** $-\frac{\sqrt{3}}{2}$ **f.** $-\sqrt{3}$

g. $\pm\frac{1}{\sqrt{3}}$ **h.** $\pm\sqrt{3}$ **i.** $\pm\frac{1}{2}$

j. $\pm\frac{1}{\sqrt{2}}$ **k.** $\pm\frac{\sqrt{3}}{2}$

2. a. 199·5, 340·5 **b.** 78·5, 281·5
c. 126·9, 306·9 **d.** 16·4, 163·6
e. 48·2, 311·8 **f.** 155·9, 335·9
g. 35·3, 144·7, 215·3, 324·7
h. 60, 120, 240, 300

3. a. 3·48, 5·94
b. 0·841, 5·44
c. 2·28, 5·43
d. 0·615, 2·53, 3·76, 5·67
e. 0·464, 2·68, 3·61, 5·82
f. 0·927, 2·21, 4·07, 5·36

Exercise 10.4

1. a. $\frac{5\pi}{4}$ **b.** $\frac{2\pi}{3}$ **c.** $\frac{13\pi}{6}$
d. $\frac{5\pi}{3}$ **e.** $\frac{3\pi}{4}$ **f.** $\frac{7\pi}{4}$
g. $\frac{4\pi}{3}$ **h.** $\frac{7\pi}{6}$ **i.** $\frac{11\pi}{6}$
j. $\frac{9\pi}{4}$

2. a. $\frac{4\pi}{3}, \frac{5\pi}{3}$ **b.** $\frac{\pi}{3}, \frac{4\pi}{3}$ **c.** $\frac{3\pi}{4}, \frac{5\pi}{4}$
d. $\frac{7\pi}{6}, \frac{11\pi}{6}$ **e.** $\frac{\pi}{6}, \frac{7\pi}{6}$ **f.** $\frac{5\pi}{4}, \frac{7\pi}{4}$
g. $\frac{5\pi}{6}, \frac{7\pi}{6}$ **h.** $\frac{2\pi}{3}, \frac{4\pi}{3}$

3. a. $\frac{\pi}{3}, \frac{2\pi}{3}, \frac{4\pi}{3}, \frac{5\pi}{3}$ **b.** $\frac{\pi}{4}, \frac{3\pi}{4}, \frac{5\pi}{4}, \frac{7\pi}{4}$
c. $\frac{\pi}{4}, \frac{3\pi}{4}, \frac{5\pi}{4}, \frac{7\pi}{4}$ **d.** $\frac{\pi}{6}, \frac{5\pi}{6}, \frac{7\pi}{6}, \frac{11\pi}{6}$
e. $\frac{\pi}{6}, \frac{5\pi}{6}, \frac{7\pi}{6}, \frac{11\pi}{6}$ **f.** $\frac{\pi}{6}, \frac{5\pi}{6}, \frac{7\pi}{6}, \frac{11\pi}{6}$

Exercise 10.5

1. a. $\frac{\pi}{4}, \frac{5\pi}{4}$ **b.** $\frac{\pi}{4}, \frac{3\pi}{4}, \frac{5\pi}{4}, \frac{7\pi}{4}$
c. $\frac{\pi}{2}, \frac{7\pi}{6}, \frac{11\pi}{6}$ **d.** $\frac{\pi}{4}, \frac{3\pi}{4}, \frac{5\pi}{4}, \frac{7\pi}{4}$
e. $0, \frac{\pi}{3}, \frac{2\pi}{3}, \pi, \frac{4\pi}{3}, \frac{5\pi}{3}, 2\pi$
f. $\frac{\pi}{12}, \frac{5\pi}{12}, \frac{13\pi}{12}, \frac{17\pi}{12}$ **g.** $\frac{\pi}{3}, \frac{2\pi}{3}, \frac{4\pi}{3}, \frac{5\pi}{3}$
h. $\frac{\pi}{8}, \frac{3\pi}{8}, \frac{5\pi}{8}, \frac{7\pi}{8}, \frac{9\pi}{8}, \frac{11\pi}{8}, \frac{13\pi}{8}, \frac{15\pi}{8}$

2. a. $P(\frac{2\pi}{3}, -0{\cdot}5)$, $Q(\pi, -0{\cdot}5)$

b. $P(\frac{\pi}{6}, -0{\cdot}5)$, $Q(\frac{\pi}{2}, -0{\cdot}5)$

c. $P(\frac{\pi}{24}, \frac{1}{\sqrt{2}})$, $Q(\frac{7\pi}{24}, \frac{1}{\sqrt{2}})$

d. $P(\frac{7\pi}{24}, -\frac{\sqrt{3}}{2})$, $Q(\frac{11\pi}{24}, -\frac{\sqrt{3}}{2})$

Exercise 10.6

1. 60, 300 **2.** 0, 60, 300, 360
3. 210, 270, 330 **4.** 90, 210, 330
5. 90, 109·5, 250·5, 270
6. 0, 41·8, 138·2, 180, 360
7. 109·5, 250·5 **8.** 11·5, 168·5, 270

Exercise 10.7

1. a. $\cos C° \cos D° + \sin C° \sin D°$
b. $\sin\theta\cos\phi + \cos\theta\sin\phi$
c. $\frac{\sqrt{3}}{2}\cos 2x - \frac{1}{2}\sin 2x$
d. $-\sin x$
e. $-\cos x°$
f. $\frac{1}{\sqrt{2}}(\cos 3x° - \sin 3x°)$
g. $\frac{1}{\sqrt{2}}(\sin\left(\frac{x}{2}\right)° - \cos\left(\frac{x}{2}\right)°)$
h. $\frac{\sqrt{3}}{2}\cos\frac{x}{2} + \frac{1}{2}\sin\frac{x}{2}$

2. Proofs

Exercise 10.8

1. a. $\frac{2}{\sqrt{5}} = \frac{2\sqrt{5}}{5}$ **b.** $\frac{\sqrt{3}}{\sqrt{19}} = \frac{\sqrt{57}}{19}$ **c.** $\sqrt{63} = 3\sqrt{7}$
d. $\frac{\sqrt{3}}{\sqrt{2}} = \frac{\sqrt{6}}{2}$ **e.** $\frac{\sqrt{3}}{\sqrt{10}} = \frac{\sqrt{30}}{10}$

2. a. $\frac{3}{5}$ **b.** $\frac{4\sqrt{3}}{7}$ **c.** $\frac{2\sqrt{46}}{5}$
d. $\frac{2\sqrt{6}}{5}$

Exercise 10.9

1. $2\sin B° \cos B°$ **2.** $2\sin\frac{\theta}{2}\cos\frac{\theta}{2}$
3. $2\sin\frac{\alpha}{2}\cos\frac{\alpha}{2}$ **4.** $2\sin 2x° \cos 2x°$
5. $2\sin\left(\frac{D}{2}\right)°\cos\left(\frac{D}{2}\right)°$ **6.** $2\sin\left(\frac{3x}{2}\right)°\cos\left(\frac{3x}{2}\right)°$
7. $2\sin\left(\frac{x}{4}\right)°\cos\left(\frac{x}{4}\right)°$ **8.** $2\sin\left(\frac{x}{3}\right)°\cos\left(\frac{x}{3}\right)°$
9. $2\sin\frac{\pi}{6}\cos\frac{\pi}{6}$

Exercise 10.10

Proofs

Exercise 10.11

1. a. (i) $\frac{1}{3}$ **(ii)** $\frac{\sqrt{8}}{3} = \frac{2\sqrt{2}}{3}$
b. (i) $\frac{3}{4}$ **(ii)** $\frac{\sqrt{7}}{4}$
c. (i) $\frac{1}{7}$ **(ii)** $\frac{\sqrt{48}}{7} = \frac{4\sqrt{3}}{7}$
d. (i) $\frac{5}{8}$ **(ii)** $\frac{\sqrt{39}}{8}$
e. (i) $\frac{3}{11}$ **(ii)** $\frac{\sqrt{112}}{11} = \frac{4\sqrt{7}}{11}$

2. a. $\frac{2\sqrt{24}}{25} = \frac{4\sqrt{6}}{25}$ **b.** $\frac{2\sqrt{200}}{45} = \frac{4\sqrt{2}}{9}$
c. $\frac{16\sqrt{57}}{121}$

3. $\frac{4\sqrt{21}}{25}$

Exercise 10.12

1. a. $\sin x° = 0$ or $\cos x° = 0$
b. $\sin x° = 0$ or $\cos x° = \frac{1}{2}$

1. c. $\cos x° = 0$ or $\sin x° = -\frac{1}{2}$
   d. $\cos x° = 0$ or $\sin x° = \frac{1}{2}$
   e. $\sin x° = 0$ or $\cos x° = -1$
   f. $\cos x° = 0$ or $\sin x° = \frac{1}{4}$

2. a. 0, 60, 180, 300, 360
   b. $\frac{\pi}{2}, \frac{7\pi}{6}, \frac{3\pi}{2}, \frac{11\pi}{6}$
   c. 30, 90, 150, 270
   d. 0, π (not 2π)
   e. 30, 90, 150, 270
   f. 0, 109·5, 180, 250·5
   g. $\frac{\pi}{2}, \frac{5\pi}{4}, \frac{3\pi}{2}, \frac{7\pi}{4}$
   h. $\pi, \frac{7\pi}{6}, 2\pi$

3. a. $2\cos^2 x - \cos x - 1 = 0$
   b. $2\sin^2 x - \sin x - 1 = 0$
   c. $2\sin^2 x + \sin x - 1 = 0$
   d. $2\cos^2 x - \cos x + 1 = 0$
   e. $2\cos^2 x - \cos x = 0$
   f. $2\sin^2 x + \sin x = 0$
   g. $4\cos^2 x + 3\cos x - 1 = 0$
   h. $6\sin^2 x + 2\sin x - 4 = 0$
   $(3\sin^2 x + \sin x - 2 = 0)$

4. a. $0, \frac{2\pi}{3}, \frac{4\pi}{3}, 2\pi$
   b. 90, 210, 330
   c. 30, 150, 270
   d. $\frac{\pi}{2}, \frac{2\pi}{3}, \frac{4\pi}{3}, \frac{3\pi}{2}$
   e. 0, 180, 210, 330, 360
   f. $\frac{7\pi}{6}, \frac{3\pi}{2}, \frac{11\pi}{6}$
   g. 30, 150, 228·6, 311·4
   h. 53·1, 120, 240, 306·9

11. CIRCLES

Exercise 11.1

1. a. $(x-2)^2 + (y-4)^2 = 36$
   b. $(x+1)^2 + (y-3)^2 = 25$
   c. $(x-2)^2 + (y+3)^2 = 4$
   d. $(x+3)^2 + (y+4)^2 = 1$
   e. $x^2 + (y+4)^2 = 4$
   f. $(x+2)^2 + y^2 = 25$
   g. $(x+3)^2 + (y-7)^2 = 3$
   h. $(x-10)^2 + (y+1)^2 = 17$

2. a. $(x-5)^2 + (y-2)^2 = 10$
   b. $(x-5)^2 + (y-10)^2 = 100$
   c. $(x+2)^2 + (y+2)^2 = 25$
   d. $(x+2)^2 + (y-8)^2 = 125$
   e. $(x-1)^2 + (y+2)^2 = 2$
   f. $(x-1)^2 + (y+4)^2 = 20$
   g. $(x-1)^2 + (y+1)^2 = \frac{1}{2}$
   or $2x^2 + 2y^2 - 4x + 4y + 3 = 0$
   h. $x^2 + (y - \frac{1}{2})^2 = \frac{5}{4}$
   or $x^2 + y^2 - y - 1 = 0$

Exercise 11.2

1. (1, –2); 2 2. (–3, 1); 3 3. (–2, 1); 3
4. (–5, 3); 6 5. (4, 4); 5 6. $(\frac{1}{2}, \frac{1}{2})$; 1
7. (3, –4); 5 8. (0, 5); 6

Exercise 11.3

1. $k > -5$ 2. $k < 1$
3. $k \leq 9$ 4. $k > -\frac{1}{2}$
5. $k < -3$ or $k > 3$ 6. $k < -2$ or $k > 2$

Exercise 11.4

1. $(x-15)^2 + (y-20)^2 = 625$
2. $(x-6)^2 + (y+8)^2 = 100$
3. $(x-12)^2 + (y-5)^2 = 169$
4. $x^2 + (y+15)^2 = 289$
5. $(x-2)^2 + (y+4)^2 = 25$
6. $(x+4)^2 + (y-4)^2 = 25$

Exercise 11.5

1. (1, 1) 2. (0, –1) 3. (1, –2)
4. (–5, 0)

Exercise 11.6

1. a. $-\frac{3}{2}$ b. $-\frac{1}{4}$ c. 2
   d. $\frac{4}{5}$ e. 1 f. $-\frac{1}{2}$
   g. $\frac{1}{6}$ h. none

2. a. $y = -x + 7$ b. $2y - x = 15$
   c. $4y + x = -4$ d. $2y + 5x = -23$
   e. $4y + 5x = -1$ f. $3y + 4x = -25$
   g. $4y + 6x = 1$
   h. $x = 5$ (parallel to the y-axis)

3. a. $\pm\frac{1}{\sqrt{2}}$ b. $\pm\sqrt{10}$ c. 3 or –1

Exercise 11.7

1. radii sum (5) > centres distance ($\sqrt{10}$).
   Not touching
2. radii sum = centres distance ($3\sqrt{2}$). Touching
3. radii sum = centres distance ($4\sqrt{5}$). Touching
4. radii sum = centres distance ($3\sqrt{10}$). Touching
5. radii sum = centres distance ($3\sqrt{13}$). Touching

UNIT 3 12. VECTORS

Exercise 12.1

1. P(1, 1, 4), Q(10, 10, 0), R(8, 8, 6), S(2, 8, 6)
2. P(11, 4, 6), Q(–11, 4, 3), R(11, 26, 6), S(–11, 26, 6)

Exercise 12.2

1. 3 **2.** 9 **3.** 15

4. 5 **5.** $\sqrt{5}$ **6.** 5

7. $\sqrt{14}$ **8.** $\sqrt{5}$ **9.** $\frac{9}{4}$

Exercise 12.3

1. a. $\boldsymbol{a} = \begin{pmatrix}1\\2\\3\end{pmatrix}$ **b.** $\boldsymbol{c} = \begin{pmatrix}-1\\3\\4\end{pmatrix}$ **c.** $\boldsymbol{d} = \begin{pmatrix}0\\-1\\\frac{1}{2}\end{pmatrix}$

d. $\boldsymbol{p} = \begin{pmatrix}-3\\0\\0\end{pmatrix}$ **e.** $\boldsymbol{e} = \begin{pmatrix}\frac{1}{2}\\-\frac{1}{2}\\\frac{3}{2}\end{pmatrix}$ **f.** $\boldsymbol{f} = \begin{pmatrix}17\\-11\\2\end{pmatrix}$

2. a. T(–1, 2, 3) **b.** U(5, 0, –1)
c. A($\frac{2}{3}$, 0, $-\frac{1}{3}$) **d.** B($\frac{1}{2}$, $-\frac{1}{2}$, 0)
e. P(1, 2, –3) **f.** Q(–5, $\frac{1}{2}$, 4)

3. a. $\boldsymbol{c}-\boldsymbol{b}$ **b.** $\boldsymbol{m}-\boldsymbol{l}$ **c.** $\boldsymbol{e}-\boldsymbol{d}$
d. $\boldsymbol{r}-\boldsymbol{a}$ **e.** $\boldsymbol{t}-\boldsymbol{p}$ **f.** $\boldsymbol{a}$
g. $\boldsymbol{l}-\boldsymbol{k}$ **h.** $\boldsymbol{w}-\boldsymbol{v}$ **i.** $-\boldsymbol{c}$

4. a. $\begin{pmatrix}7\\-1\\-1\end{pmatrix}$ **b.** $\begin{pmatrix}-3\\-2\\3\end{pmatrix}$ **c.** $\begin{pmatrix}-4\\-10\\2\end{pmatrix}$

d. $\begin{pmatrix}-1\\-1\\-1\end{pmatrix}$ **e.** $\begin{pmatrix}-1\\2\\6\end{pmatrix}$ **f.** $\begin{pmatrix}5\\10\\-8\end{pmatrix}$

g. $\begin{pmatrix}\frac{1}{2}\\-\frac{1}{2}\\\frac{1}{2}\end{pmatrix}$ **h.** $\begin{pmatrix}\sqrt{2}\\-\sqrt{2}\\0\end{pmatrix}$

5. a. $\begin{pmatrix}3\\6\\3\end{pmatrix}$ **b.** $\begin{pmatrix}1\\-5\\2\end{pmatrix}$ **c.** $\begin{pmatrix}-2\\-11\\-1\end{pmatrix}$

d. $\begin{pmatrix}-1\\5\\-2\end{pmatrix}$

6. a. (i) $\begin{pmatrix}4\\5\\-4\end{pmatrix}$ **(ii)** $\begin{pmatrix}4\\5\\-4\end{pmatrix}$ **(iii)** $\begin{pmatrix}-4\\1\\-5\end{pmatrix}$

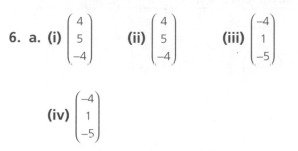

(iv) $\begin{pmatrix}-4\\1\\-5\end{pmatrix}$

b. parallelogram

Exercise 12.4

1. $\overrightarrow{BC} = 3\overrightarrow{AB}$, B is shared; 1:3
2. $\overrightarrow{QR} = 2\overrightarrow{PQ}$, Q is shared; 1:2
3. $\overrightarrow{TU} = \frac{1}{2}\overrightarrow{ST}$, T is shared; 2:1
4. $\overrightarrow{WX} = \frac{2}{3}\overrightarrow{VW}$, W is shared; 3:2
5. $\overrightarrow{EF} = \frac{3}{2}\overrightarrow{DE}$, E is shared; 2:3
6. $\overrightarrow{KL} = \frac{5}{4}\overrightarrow{JK}$, K is shared; 4:5
7. $\overrightarrow{NP} = \frac{2}{5}\overrightarrow{MN}$, N is shared; 5:2
8. $\overrightarrow{HI} = \frac{1}{2}\overrightarrow{GH}$, H is shared; 2:1

Exercise 12.5

1. P(1, 1, 2) **2.** Q(5, 1, 2)
3. R(–3, 2, –1) **4.** A($-\frac{1}{2}$, $\frac{1}{2}$, $\frac{1}{2}$)

Exercise 12.6

1. a. 70·9 **b.** 45·5 **c.** 103·3

2. 33·1°

3. ∠A = 61·9°, ∠B = 28·1°, ∠C = 90°

Exercise 12.7

1. a. 1 **b.** 2 **c.** 2
d. 2 **e.** 13 **f.** –3

2. $m = -2$ or 3

3. $\overrightarrow{AB}.\overrightarrow{AC} = 0$ so ∠BAC = 90°

4. $\overrightarrow{PQ}.\overrightarrow{PR} = 0$ so ∠QPR = 90°
Area = 9 unit^2

Exercise 12.8

1. a. 3 **b.** $\sqrt{3}$ **c.** 25
d. 1

2. 4

3. a. both $\sqrt{2}$ **b.** 2

4. 24

Exercise 12.9

1. a. $\begin{pmatrix}3\\-2\\5\end{pmatrix}$ **b.** $\begin{pmatrix}4\\-\sqrt{2}\\0\end{pmatrix}$ **c.** $\begin{pmatrix}-1\\-2\\8\end{pmatrix}$

d. $\begin{pmatrix}0\\-\sqrt{5}\\-2\end{pmatrix}$ **e.** $\begin{pmatrix}1\\1\\1\end{pmatrix}$ **f.** $\begin{pmatrix}1\\-1\\-1\end{pmatrix}$

g. $\begin{pmatrix}0\\18\\-\sqrt{11}\end{pmatrix}$ **h.** $\begin{pmatrix}0\\-\sqrt{2}\\0\end{pmatrix}$

2. a. 3 **b.** 7 **c.** 9
d. 5 **e.** 6 **f.** 5
g. 3 **h.** 3 **i.** $\sqrt{5}$
j. 4

3. a. $-\frac{1}{3}\boldsymbol{i} - \frac{2}{3}\boldsymbol{j} + \frac{2}{3}\boldsymbol{k}$ **b.** $\frac{1}{3}\boldsymbol{i} - \frac{2}{3}\boldsymbol{j} + \frac{2}{3}\boldsymbol{k}$
c. $-\frac{6}{7}\boldsymbol{i} + \frac{3}{7}\boldsymbol{j} - \frac{2}{7}\boldsymbol{k}$

13. FURTHER DIFFERENTIATION AND INTEGRATION

Exercise 13.1

1. a. $\cos x$ **b.** $-\sin x$
c. $3\cos x$ **d.** $2x - 2\cos x$
e. $2 + \sin x$ **f.** $6x + 4\sin x$
g. $-\frac{1}{x^2} - \frac{1}{2}\cos x$ **h.** $-\frac{3}{x^2} + \frac{2}{3}\sin x$
i. $10\sin x$

2. a. $\frac{5x^4}{4} + \frac{x^2}{2} - \cos x + C$
b. $2x^2 - \sin x + C$
c. $x^3 - x^2 + \cos x + C$
d. $\frac{3x^4}{2} - 2x^3 + \sin x + C$
e. $2x^5 + 2\sin x + C$
f. $\frac{5x^3}{3} - \frac{x^2}{2} + 3\cos x + C$
g. $2x^4 - 3x^3 - 2\sin x + C$
h. $5x^2 + 3x^4 - 4\cos x + C$

Exercise 13.2

1. a. $\frac{1}{2}$ unit² **b.** $\frac{1}{2}$ unit² **c.** $\frac{1}{4}$ unit²
d. $\frac{1}{4}$ unit² **e.** $\frac{\sqrt{3}}{4}$ unit² **f.** $\frac{\sqrt{3}-1}{4}$ unit²

2. a. 1 unit² **b.** $\frac{1}{2}$ unit²

3. $\frac{4+\sqrt{2}}{4}$ unit² ($\frac{2+\sqrt{2}}{4}$ unit² above and $\frac{1}{2}$ unit² below)

Exercise 13.3

1. $3(\sin x + x)^2(\cos x + 1)$
2. $2(x^2 - \cos x)(2x + \sin x)$
3. $\frac{2x+1}{2\sqrt{x^2+x}}$ **4.** $\frac{\cos x}{2\sqrt{\sin x - 3}}$
5. $-\frac{3\cos x}{2\sqrt{5-3\sin x}}$ **6.** $-2\cos x \sin x$
7. $\frac{\sin x}{2\left(\sqrt{\cos x}\right)^3}$ **8.** $-\frac{\cos x}{2\left(\sqrt{\sin x}\right)^3}$
9. $-\frac{\sin x}{\sqrt{2\cos x - 3}}$ **10.** $\frac{\sin x}{\cos^2 x}$
11. $\frac{\sin x - \cos x}{\left(\sin x + \cos x\right)^2}$ **12.** $-\frac{2\cos x}{\sin^3 x}$

Exercise 13.4

1. a. $\frac{(3x-1)^3}{9} + C$ **b.** $\frac{(5x+1)^4}{20} + C$
c. $-\frac{(3-2x)^3}{6} + C$ **d.** $\frac{(4+6x)^5}{30} + C$
e. $\frac{(3x+4)^4}{6} + C$ **f.** $-\frac{(5-2x)^3}{2} + C$
g. $-\frac{(2-x)^5}{5} + C$ **h.** $-\frac{3(7-x)^4}{2} + C$

2. a. $\frac{26}{3}$ **b.** $\frac{13}{3}$ **c.** 20
d. $\frac{1}{2}$ **e.** $\frac{43}{3}$ **f.** $\frac{31}{10}$
g. 19 **h.** $\frac{1}{2}$

14. LOGARITHMIC AND EXPONENTIAL FUNCTIONS

Exercise 14.1

1. a. $\log_{10}92 = x$ **b.** $\log_e 4 = -y$
c. $\log_e 14{\cdot}1 = 2t$ **d.** $\log_{10}y = 0{\cdot}5t$
e. $\log_e 0{\cdot}002 = 1{\cdot}5t$ **f.** $\log_e B_3 = -5t$
g. $\log_e 0{\cdot}5 = -2x$ **h.** $\log_{10}A_1 = x + t$

2. a. $x = 2^3$ **b.** $10 = 5^x$ **c.** $t = 10^4$
d. $A = e^B$ **e.** $V_0 = m^k$ **f.** $2A + 1 = b^T$

3. a. 7·39 **b.** 1260 **c.** 1·10
d. 1·72 **e.** 1·03 **f.** 1·67
g. −3·51 **h.** −0·824

4. a. 0·0134 **b.** 0·00954 **c.** 0·0173
d. 0·0126 **e.** 0·00793 **f.** 0·00524
g. 0·0132 **h.** 0·0146

5. a. $k = 0{\cdot}03764$; 18·4 days
b. $k = 0{\cdot}03144$; 22·0 hours
c. **(i)** 2·51 years **(ii)** 24 400 years
(iii) 12·2 years **(iv)** 5780 years

Exercise 14.2

1. a. 2 **b.** 1 **c.** 1 **d.** 1

2. a. 2 **b.** 1 **c.** 2 **d.** 6

3. a. 1·58 **b.** 1·11 **c.** 1·77 **d.** −1·16 **e.** −0·356 **f.** 0·315

4. a. 9·97 **b.** −2·10 **c.** 0·208 **d.** 0·231 **e.** 2·86 **f.** 8·04

Exercise 14.3

1. a. $a = 3, b = 1$ **b.** $a = \frac{1}{2}, b = 3$

2. a. $a = 2, b = 1$ **b.** $a = 2, b = 2$

3. a. $y = 2\log_2(x - 1)$ **b.** $y = \frac{5}{2}\log_2(x + 1)$

4. $a = 8, b = 5$

Exercise 14.4

1. a. $y = 2x + 1{\cdot}1$ **b.** $y = 0{\cdot}5x + 2{\cdot}5$
c. $y = -2x + 3$ **d.** $y = 1{\cdot}5x + 9{\cdot}5$

2. a. $Y = 2X + 0{\cdot}3$ **b.** $Y = -0{\cdot}5X + 3$

3. a. $a = 4{\cdot}48, b = 2$ **b.** $a = 2{\cdot}23, b = 3{\cdot}6$
c. $a = 9{\cdot}97, b = 0{\cdot}5$

4. $a = 1{\cdot}35, b = 1{\cdot}2$

5. a. $Y = 0{\cdot}5X + 0{\cdot}681$
b. $a = 1{\cdot}98, b = 0{\cdot}5$
(or approximately: $y = 2x^{\frac{1}{2}} = 2\sqrt{x}$)

15. THE WAVE FUNCTION

Exercise 15.1

1. a. 26·6 **b.** 56·3 **c.** 60 **d.** 45

2. a. $\sqrt{5}$ **b.** $\sqrt{34}$ **c.** $\sqrt{7}$ **d.** $\sqrt{3}$

3. a. $\alpha = 53{\cdot}1$; $k = 5$
b. $\alpha = 69{\cdot}3$; $k = 2\sqrt{2}$
c. $\alpha = 45$; $k = 5\sqrt{2}$
d. $\alpha = 69{\cdot}4$; $k = \sqrt{73}$
e. $\alpha = 37{\cdot}8$; $k = 2\sqrt{2}$
f. $\alpha = 54{\cdot}7$; $k = \sqrt{15}$

Exercise 15.2

1. $5\cos(x - 53{\cdot}1)°$ **2.** $13\sin(x + 67{\cdot}4)°$
3. $\sqrt{5}\sin(x - 63{\cdot}4)°$ **4.** $\sqrt{29}\cos(x + 68{\cdot}2)°$
5. $2\cos(x - 30)°$ **6.** $2\sin(x - 45)°$

Exercise 15.3

1. a. 75·9°, 354·1° **b.** 34·8°, 175·8°
c. 117·7°, 223·9° **d.** 172·2°, 318·6°

2. a. $\sqrt{10}\cos(x - 18{\cdot}4)°$ **b.** 117·5°, 279·3°

3. a. $2\sin(x - 30)°$ **b.** 53·6°, 186·4°

4. 64·3°, 189·5°

Exercise 15.4

1. a. Max 2, $x = 70$; Min −2, $x = 250$
b. Max 3, $x = 30$; Min −3, $x = 210$
c. Max $\sqrt{2}$, $x = 350$; Min $-\sqrt{2}$, $x = 170$
d. Max $2\sqrt{3}$, $x = 350$; Min $-2\sqrt{3}$, $x = 170$
e. Max 10, $x = 190$; Min −10, $x = 10$
f. Max 2·6, $x = 240$; Min −2·6, $x = 60$

2. a. Max 25, $\theta = 16{\cdot}3$; Min −25, $\theta = 196{\cdot}3$
b. Max 13, $\theta = 337{\cdot}4$; Min −13, $\theta = 157{\cdot}4$
c. Max 5, $\theta = 143{\cdot}1$; Min −5, $\theta = 323{\cdot}1$
d. Max 13, $\theta = 22{\cdot}6$; Min −13, $\theta = 202{\cdot}6$
e. Max $\sqrt{10}$, $\theta = 288{\cdot}4$; Min $-\sqrt{10}$, $\theta = 108{\cdot}4$
f. Max $\sqrt{3}$, $\theta = 33{\cdot}7$; Min $-\sqrt{3}$, $\theta = 213{\cdot}7$

SOLUTIONS TO PRACTICE EXAM A

Each (speech bubble) refers back to an exercise which practises the skill or technique occurring in the solution at that point. Use these references to identify your weaknesses and use the corresponding exercises to practise those skills.

SOLUTIONS TO EXAM A PAPER 1

1. Coordinates of M:

$M\left(\frac{-1+3}{2}, \frac{3+(-1)}{2}\right) = M\left(\frac{2}{2}, \frac{2}{2}\right) = M(1, 1)$ p.7 Ex 1.11

Gradient of line:

$m_{BC} = \frac{3-0}{-1-(-2)} = \frac{3}{-1+2} = \frac{3}{1} = 3$ p.5 Ex 1.1

So $m_{\perp} = -\frac{1}{3}$ p.6 Ex 1.5

Equation of line:

Point on line is M(1, 1) and gradient is $-\frac{1}{3}$

Required equation is $y - 1 = -\frac{1}{3}(x - 1)$

So $3y - 3 = -(x - 1)$

So $3y - 3 = -x + 1$

giving $3y + x = 4$ p.6 Ex 1.7

2. a. The multiplier a must lie between -1 and 1, i.e. $-1 < a < 1$, for a limit to exist. p.19 Ex 6.2

b. Since $u_{n+1} = au_n + b$ and $u_1 = 5$

Then $u_2 = au_1 + b = a \times 5 + b = 5a + b$

So $5a + b = 8$

also $u_3 = au_2 + b$

$= a \times 8 + b$

$= 8a + b$

So $8a + b = 9{\cdot}5$ p.19 Ex 6.1 Q2

Now solve $\left.\begin{aligned} 5a + b &= 8 \\ 8a + b &= 9{\cdot}5 \end{aligned}\right\} \Rightarrow 3a = 1{\cdot}5$

So $a = \frac{1{\cdot}5}{3} = 0{\cdot}5$

So $5a + b = 8$

gives $5 \times 0{\cdot}5 + b = 8$

So $2{\cdot}5 + b = 8 \Rightarrow b = 5{\cdot}5$ p.6 Ex 1.9 Q1

c. The recurrence relation is

$u_{n+1} = 0{\cdot}5u_n + 5{\cdot}5$

Let the limit of the sequence be L then

$L = 0{\cdot}5L + 5{\cdot}5$

$L - 0{\cdot}5L = 5{\cdot}5 \Rightarrow 0{\cdot}5L = 5{\cdot}5$

$\Rightarrow L = \frac{5{\cdot}5}{0{\cdot}5} = 11$ p.19 Ex 6.3

3. a. $f(x) = 4x^3 - 12x^2 + 5x + 6$

Divide $f(x)$ by $x - 2$:

2	4	−12	5	6
		8	−8	−6
	4	4	3	0

So $x - 2$ is a factor p.20 Ex 7.1

3. a. (cont.) This gives:

$f(x) = (x - 2)(4x^2 - 4x - 3)$

$= (x - 2)(2x - 3)(2x + 1)$

The other factors are:

$2x - 3$ and $2x + 1$ p.20 Ex 7.2

b. On the x-axis $y = 0$ (i.e. $f(x) = 0$)

So $(x - 2)(2x - 3)(2x + 1) = 0$

$x - 2 = 0$ or $2x - 3 = 0$ or $2x + 1 = 0$

$x = 2$ or $x = \frac{3}{2}$ or $x = -\frac{1}{2}$ p.20 Ex 7.3 Q1

The required x-axis intercepts are:

$(2, 0)$, $(\frac{3}{2}, 0)$ and $(-\frac{1}{2}, 0)$

4. From $\sin x = \frac{2}{3}$, construct a triangle:

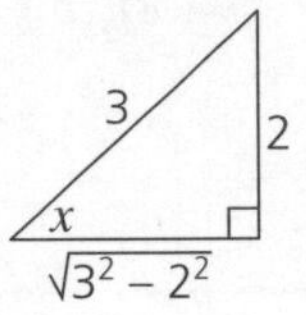

$\sqrt{3^2 - 2^2} = \sqrt{9 - 4} = \sqrt{5}$

giving $\cos x = \frac{\sqrt{5}}{3}$ p.28 Ex 10.8 Q1

Now $\cos(x + \frac{\pi}{6}) = \cos x \cos \frac{\pi}{6} - \sin x \sin \frac{\pi}{6}$

Exact values:

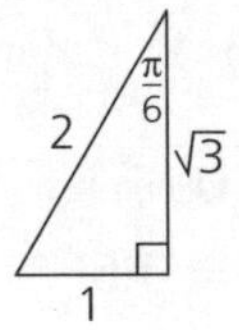

$\cos \frac{\pi}{6} = \frac{\sqrt{3}}{2}$

$\sin \frac{\pi}{6} = \frac{1}{2}$ p.12 Ex 4.2

So $\cos(x + \frac{\pi}{6}) = \frac{\sqrt{5}}{3} \times \frac{\sqrt{3}}{2} - \frac{2}{3} \times \frac{1}{2}$

$= \frac{\sqrt{15}}{6} - \frac{2}{6}$

$= \frac{\sqrt{15} - 2}{6}$ p.27 Ex 10.7

5. a.

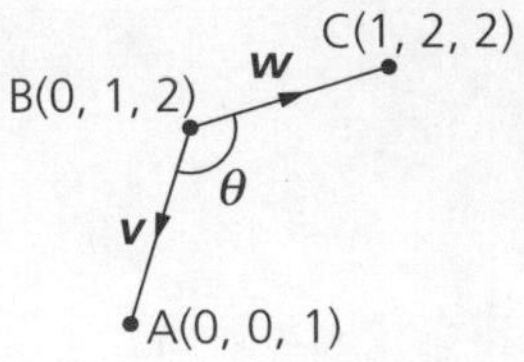

Use $\cos \theta = \frac{\boldsymbol{v}.\boldsymbol{w}}{|\boldsymbol{v}||\boldsymbol{w}|}$

$\boldsymbol{v} = \overrightarrow{BA} = \boldsymbol{a} - \boldsymbol{b} = \begin{pmatrix}0\\0\\1\end{pmatrix} - \begin{pmatrix}0\\1\\2\end{pmatrix} = \begin{pmatrix}0\\-1\\-1\end{pmatrix}$

$\boldsymbol{w} = \overrightarrow{BC} = \boldsymbol{c} - \boldsymbol{b} = \begin{pmatrix}1\\2\\2\end{pmatrix} - \begin{pmatrix}0\\1\\2\end{pmatrix} = \begin{pmatrix}1\\1\\0\end{pmatrix}$ p.33 Ex 12.3

5. a. (cont.)

$$|\boldsymbol{v}| = \left|\begin{pmatrix}0\\-1\\-1\end{pmatrix}\right| = \sqrt{0^2+(-1)^2+(-1)^2} = \sqrt{2}$$

$$|\boldsymbol{w}| = \left|\begin{pmatrix}1\\1\\0\end{pmatrix}\right| = \sqrt{1^2+1^2+0^2} = \sqrt{2}$$

p.33 Ex 12.2

and $\boldsymbol{v}.\boldsymbol{w} = \begin{pmatrix}0\\-1\\-1\end{pmatrix}.\begin{pmatrix}1\\1\\0\end{pmatrix}$

$= 0 \times 1 + (-1) \times 1 + (-1) \times 0 = -1$

so $\cos\theta = \dfrac{\boldsymbol{v}.\boldsymbol{w}}{|\boldsymbol{v}||\boldsymbol{w}|} = \dfrac{-1}{\sqrt{2}\times\sqrt{2}} = -\dfrac{1}{2}$

i.e. $\cos ABC = -\dfrac{1}{2}$

p.35 Ex 12.6

b. $M\left(\dfrac{0+1}{2}, \dfrac{0+2}{2}, \dfrac{1+2}{2}\right) = M\left(\dfrac{1}{2}, 1, \dfrac{3}{2}\right)$

Consider B(0, 1, 2), $M\left(\dfrac{1}{2}, 1, \dfrac{3}{2}\right)$ and D(2, 1, 0)

$$\overrightarrow{BM} = \boldsymbol{m} - \boldsymbol{b} = \begin{pmatrix}\frac{1}{2}\\1\\\frac{3}{2}\end{pmatrix} - \begin{pmatrix}0\\1\\2\end{pmatrix} = \begin{pmatrix}\frac{1}{2}\\0\\-\frac{1}{2}\end{pmatrix}$$

$$\overrightarrow{MD} = \boldsymbol{d} - \boldsymbol{m} = \begin{pmatrix}2\\1\\0\end{pmatrix} - \begin{pmatrix}\frac{1}{2}\\1\\\frac{3}{2}\end{pmatrix} = \begin{pmatrix}\frac{3}{2}\\0\\-\frac{3}{2}\end{pmatrix} = 3\begin{pmatrix}\frac{1}{2}\\0\\-\frac{1}{2}\end{pmatrix}$$

so $\overrightarrow{MD} = 3\overrightarrow{BM}$

Since M is a shared point this means B, M and D are collinear.

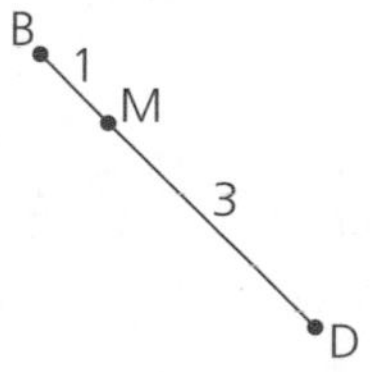

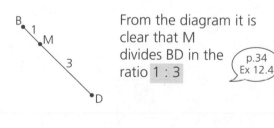

From the diagram it is clear that M divides BD in the ratio 1 : 3

p.34 Ex 12.4

6. Consider $x^2 + y^2 - 2x - 6y + 1 = 0$

Centre is (1, 3)

Radius $= \sqrt{1^2 + 3^2 - 1}$

$= \sqrt{9} = 3$

p.31 Ex 11.2

Now use this information on the given diagram:

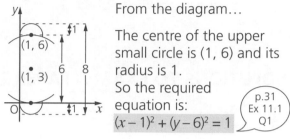

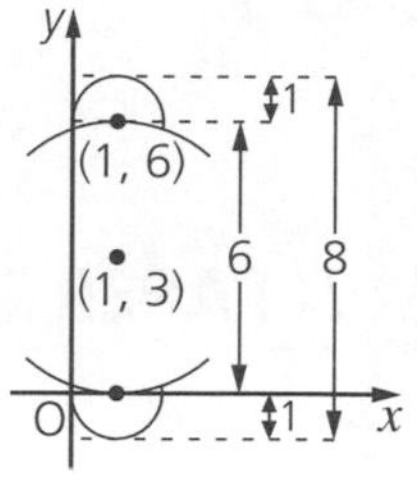

From the diagram…

The centre of the upper small circle is (1, 6) and its radius is 1.

So the required equation is:

$(x-1)^2 + (y-6)^2 = 1$

p.31 Ex 11.1 Q1

7. $\displaystyle\int_{-2}^{-1} \frac{6x^3 - x}{3x^3}\,dx = \int_{-2}^{-1} \frac{6x^3}{3x^3} - \frac{x}{3x^3}\,dx$

$\displaystyle = \int_{-2}^{-1} 2 - \frac{x^{-2}}{3}\,dx$

$\displaystyle = \left[2x - \frac{x^{-1}}{3\times(-1)}\right]_{-2}^{-1}$

$\displaystyle = \left[2x + \frac{1}{3x}\right]_{-2}^{-1}$

$\displaystyle = \left(2\times(-1) + \frac{1}{3\times(-1)}\right) - \left(2\times(-2) + \frac{1}{3\times(-2)}\right)$

$= -2 - \frac{1}{3} + 4 + \frac{1}{6} = 1\frac{5}{6}$

p.23-24 Ex 9.3 Ex 9.4

8. Sketch of $y = 3\sin(x + 30)°$:

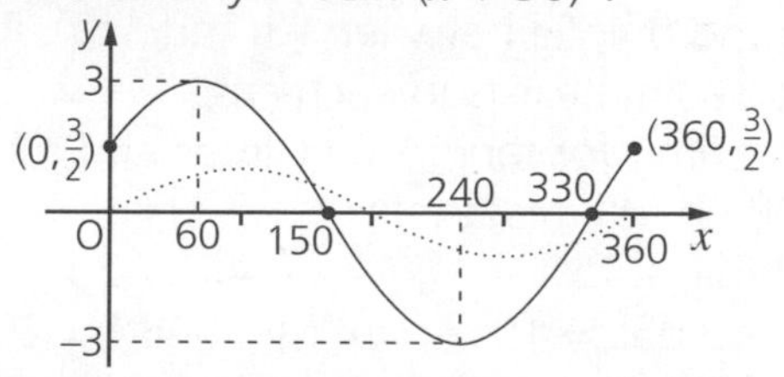

[3sin ( ) gives an amplitude of 3

…sin (… + 30)° moves the sine graph 30° to the left.

When $x = 0$, $y = 3\sin(0 + 30)° = 3\sin 30°$

$= 3 \times \frac{1}{2} = \frac{3}{2}$

So the y-intercept is $(0, \frac{3}{2})$.]

p.13 Ex 4.5

9. $y = \dfrac{1}{\sin^2 x} = \dfrac{1}{(\sin x)^2} = (\sin x)^{-2}$

So $\dfrac{dy}{dx} = -2(\sin x)^{-3} \times \cos x = -\dfrac{2\cos x}{\sin^3 x}$

p.38 Ex 13.3

10. a. For the x-axis intercept set $y = 0$
So $0 = 2 - \log_3(x + 1)$
$\Rightarrow \log_3(x + 1) = 2 \Rightarrow x + 1 = 3^2$
$x = 3^2 - 1 = 9 - 1 = 8$
So the x-coordinate of A is 8

p.39 Ex 14.1 Q2

b. For the y-axis intercept set $x = 0$
So $y = 2 - \log_3(0 + 1) = 2 - \log_3 1$
$= 2 - 0 = 2$
So the y-coordinate of B is 2

10. c. For point C solve:

$$\left.\begin{array}{l} y = 3 \\ y = 2 - \log_3(x+1) \end{array}\right\} \Rightarrow 3 = 2 - \log_3(x + 1)$$

$\Rightarrow \log_3(x + 1) = -1$
$\Rightarrow x + 1 = 3^{-1}$
$\Rightarrow x + 1 = \frac{1}{3}$
so $x = \frac{1}{3} - 1$
$= -\frac{2}{3}$
thus $C(-\frac{2}{3}, 3)$

p.39 Ex 14.1 Q2

SOLUTIONS TO EXAM A PAPER 2

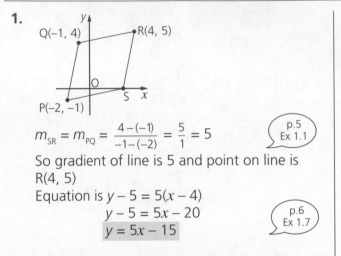

1.

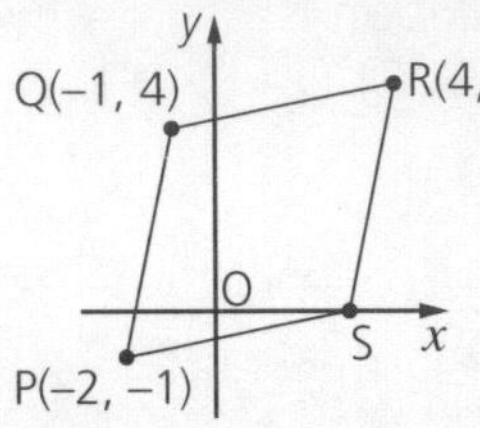

$m_{SR} = m_{PQ} = \dfrac{4-(-1)}{-1-(-2)} = \dfrac{5}{1} = 5$

p.5 Ex 1.1

So gradient of line is 5 and point on line is R(4, 5)
Equation is $y - 5 = 5(x - 4)$
$y - 5 = 5x - 20$
$y = 5x - 15$

p.6 Ex 1.7

2. After n days let the amount of pollutant in tank A be A_n litres and in tank B be B_n litres. The recurrence relations which model this situation are:
$A_{n+1} = 0{\cdot}65A_n + 15$ and $B_{n+1} = 0{\cdot}4B_n + 25$

In both cases the multipliers, namely 0·65 and 0·4, lie between –1 and 1 and so a limit exists in each case.

p.19 Ex 6.2

Let the limit for tank A be L litres and for tank B be M litres, then:

$L = 0{\cdot}65L + 15$	$M = 0{\cdot}4M + 25$
$\Rightarrow L - 0{\cdot}65L = 15$	$\Rightarrow M - 0{\cdot}4M = 25$
$\Rightarrow 0{\cdot}35L = 15$	$\Rightarrow 0{\cdot}6M = 25$
$\Rightarrow L = \frac{15}{0{\cdot}35}$	$\Rightarrow M = \frac{25}{0{\cdot}6}$
$\doteq 42{\cdot}9$	$\doteq 41{\cdot}7$

p.19 Ex 6.3

In the long run tank B will contain 41·7 litres (to 3 sig figs) of pollutant, approximately 1·2 litres less than the amount of pollutant in tank A.

p.19 Ex 6.4

3. a. $f(x) = 3x^2 - 6x + 2$
$= 3(x^2 - 2x + \frac{2}{3})$
$= 3[(x - 1)(x - 1) - 1 + \frac{2}{3}]$
$= 3[(x - 1)^2 - \frac{1}{3}]$
$= 3(x - 1)^2 - 1$

p.11 Ex 3.7 Q2

p.11 Ex 3.7 Q3

[compare $a(x + b)^2 + c$, so $a = 3$, $b = -1$ and $c = -1$]

3. b. The minimum value of $(x - 1)^2$ is 0 when $x = 1$, so the minimum value of $f(x) = 3(x - 1)^2 - 1$ is $3 \times 0 - 1 = -1$ when $x = 1$
i.e. the minimum turning point of the graph $y = f(x)$ is $(1, -1)$

4. a. Consider $y = x^3 - 2x + 1$
$\Rightarrow \dfrac{dy}{dx} = 3x^2 - 2$
when $x = 1$ (at point P) then
$\dfrac{dy}{dx} = 3 \times 1^2 - 2 = 3 - 2 = 1$

The gradient of the tangent is 1, point on tangent is P(1, 0), so the equation is:
$y - 0 = 1(x - 1)$
$\Rightarrow y = x - 1$

p.17 Ex 5.8

b. To find Q, the point of intersection, solve:

$$\left.\begin{array}{l} y = x^3 - 2x + 1 \\ y = x - 1 \end{array}\right\} \Rightarrow x^3 - 2x + 1 = x - 1$$
$$\Rightarrow x^3 - 3x + 2 = 0$$

To factorise $x^3 - 3x + 2$ try dividing it by $x - 1$:

1	1	0	–3	2
		1	1	–2
	1	1	–2	0

So $x^3 - 3x + 2 = (x - 1)(x^2 + x - 2)$
$= (x - 1)(x + 2)(x - 1)$

p.20 Ex 7.1 Ex 7.2

The equation becomes:
$(x - 1)(x + 2)(x - 1) = 0$
So $x = 1$ or $x = -2$

p.20 Ex 7.3 Q1

$x = 1$ gives the known point of intersection P(1, 0)
when $x = -2$ then $y = x - 1$
$= -2 - 1$
$= -3$
so $Q(-2, -3)$

p.20 Ex 7.3 Q2, Q3

4. c.

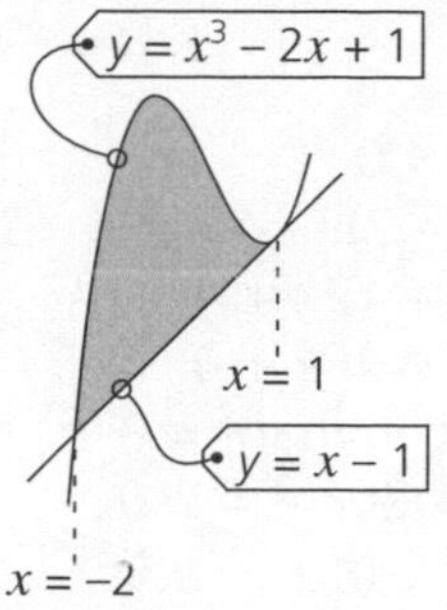

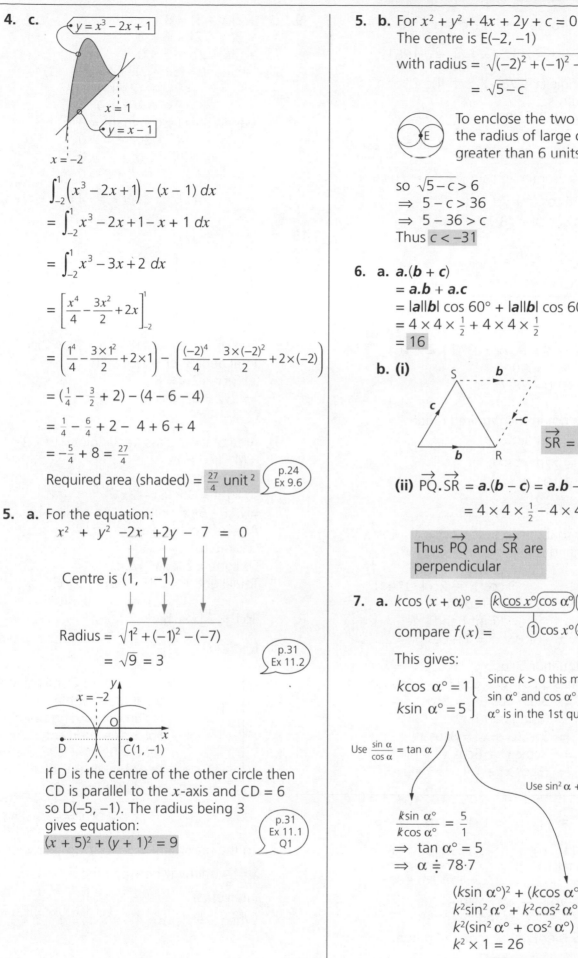

$$\int_{-2}^{1} \left(x^3 - 2x + 1\right) - (x - 1)\, dx$$

$$= \int_{-2}^{1} x^3 - 2x + 1 - x + 1\, dx$$

$$= \int_{-2}^{1} x^3 - 3x + 2\, dx$$

$$= \left[\frac{x^4}{4} - \frac{3x^2}{2} + 2x\right]_{-2}^{1}$$

$$= \left(\frac{1^4}{4} - \frac{3\times 1^2}{2} + 2\times 1\right) - \left(\frac{(-2)^4}{4} - \frac{3\times(-2)^2}{2} + 2\times(-2)\right)$$

$$= \left(\tfrac{1}{4} - \tfrac{3}{2} + 2\right) - (4 - 6 - 4)$$

$$= \tfrac{1}{4} - \tfrac{6}{4} + 2 - 4 + 6 + 4$$

$$= -\tfrac{5}{4} + 8 = \tfrac{27}{4}$$

Required area (shaded) = $\frac{27}{4}$ unit ^{2}

p.24 Ex 9.6

5. a. For the equation:

$x^2 + y^2 - 2x + 2y - 7 = 0$

Centre is (1, −1)

Radius = $\sqrt{1^2 + (-1)^2 - (-7)}$

$= \sqrt{9} = 3$

p.31 Ex 11.2

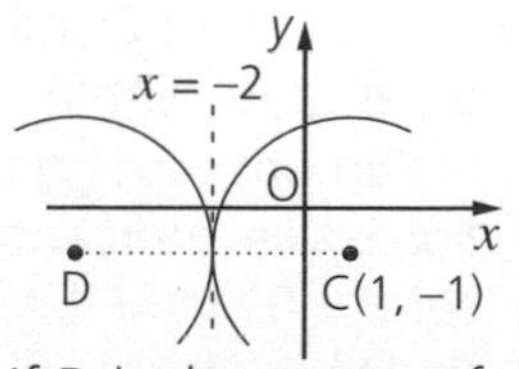

If D is the centre of the other circle then CD is parallel to the x-axis and CD = 6 so D(−5, −1). The radius being 3 gives equation:

$(x + 5)^2 + (y + 1)^2 = 9$

p.31 Ex 11.1 Q1

5. b. For $x^2 + y^2 + 4x + 2y + c = 0$

The centre is E(−2, −1)

with radius = $\sqrt{(-2)^2 + (-1)^2 - c}$

$= \sqrt{5 - c}$

p.31 Ex 11.2

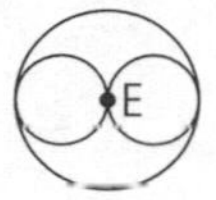

To enclose the two circles, the radius of large circle is greater than 6 units

so $\sqrt{5 - c} > 6$

$\Rightarrow\ 5 - c > 36$

$\Rightarrow\ 5 - 36 > c$

Thus $c < -31$

p.31 Ex 11.3

6. a. $\boldsymbol{a}.(\boldsymbol{b} + \boldsymbol{c})$

$= \boldsymbol{a}.\boldsymbol{b} + \boldsymbol{a}.\boldsymbol{c}$

$= |\boldsymbol{a}||\boldsymbol{b}| \cos 60° + |\boldsymbol{a}||\boldsymbol{b}| \cos 60°$

$= 4 \times 4 \times \frac{1}{2} + 4 \times 4 \times \frac{1}{2}$

$= 16$

p.35 Ex 12.8

b. (i)

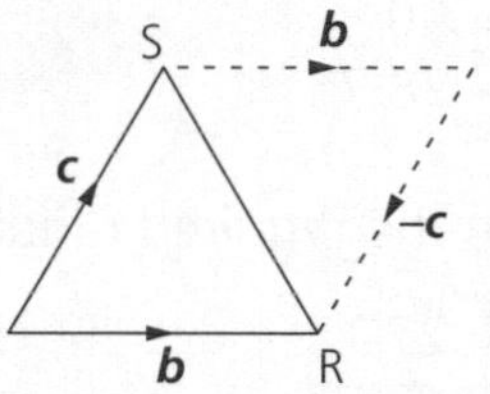

$\overrightarrow{SR} = \boldsymbol{b} - \boldsymbol{c}$

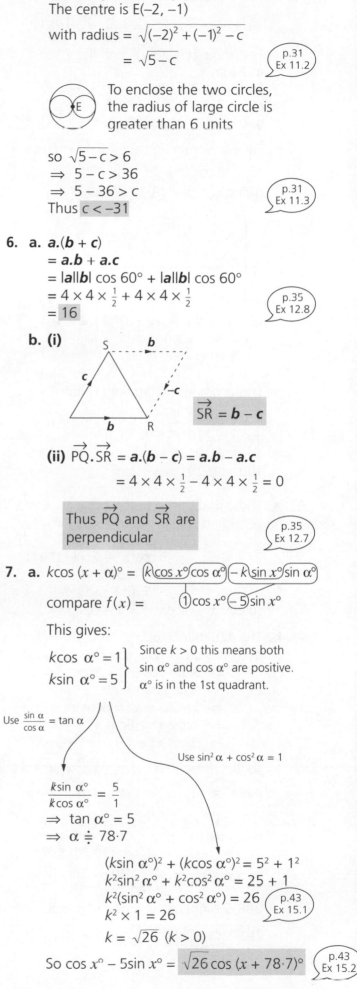

(ii) $\overrightarrow{PQ}.\overrightarrow{SR} = \boldsymbol{a}.(\boldsymbol{b} - \boldsymbol{c}) = \boldsymbol{a}.\boldsymbol{b} - \boldsymbol{a}.\boldsymbol{c}$

$= 4 \times 4 \times \frac{1}{2} - 4 \times 4 \times \frac{1}{2} = 0$

Thus $\overrightarrow{PQ}$ and $\overrightarrow{SR}$ are perpendicular

p.35 Ex 12.7

7. a. $k\cos(x + \alpha)° = k\cos x° \cos \alpha° - k\sin x° \sin \alpha°$

compare $f(x) = 1\cos x° - 5\sin x°$

This gives:

$k\cos \alpha° = 1$
$k\sin \alpha° = 5$

Since $k > 0$ this means both $\sin \alpha°$ and $\cos \alpha°$ are positive. $\alpha°$ is in the 1st quadrant.

Use $\frac{\sin \alpha}{\cos \alpha} = \tan \alpha$

$$\frac{k\sin \alpha°}{k\cos \alpha°} = \frac{5}{1}$$

$\Rightarrow\ \tan \alpha° = 5$

$\Rightarrow\ \alpha \doteqdot 78{\cdot}7$

Use $\sin^2 \alpha + \cos^2 \alpha = 1$

$(k\sin \alpha°)^2 + (k\cos \alpha°)^2 = 5^2 + 1^2$

$k^2\sin^2 \alpha° + k^2\cos^2 \alpha° = 25 + 1$

$k^2(\sin^2 \alpha° + \cos^2 \alpha°) = 26$

$k^2 \times 1 = 26$

$k = \sqrt{26}\ (k > 0)$

p.43 Ex 15.1

So $\cos x° - 5\sin x° = \sqrt{26}\cos(x + 78{\cdot}7)°$

p.43 Ex 15.2

7. b. $f(x) = 1$ becomes $\sqrt{26}\cos(x + 78{\cdot}7)° = 1$

$\Rightarrow \cos(x + 78{\cdot}7)° = \frac{1}{\sqrt{26}} = 0{\cdot}1961\ldots$

The angle $(x + 78{\cdot}7)°$ is in the 1st or 4th quadrants.

So $x + 78{\cdot}7 = 78{\cdot}7$
or $x + 78{\cdot}7 = 360 - 78{\cdot}7$
giving $x = 0$ or $x = 202{\cdot}6$

p.43 Ex 15.3

c. For x-axis intercept set $y = 0$ i.e. $f(x) = 0$
so $\sqrt{26}\cos(x + 78{\cdot}7)° = 0$
giving $\cos(x + 78{\cdot}7)° = 0$

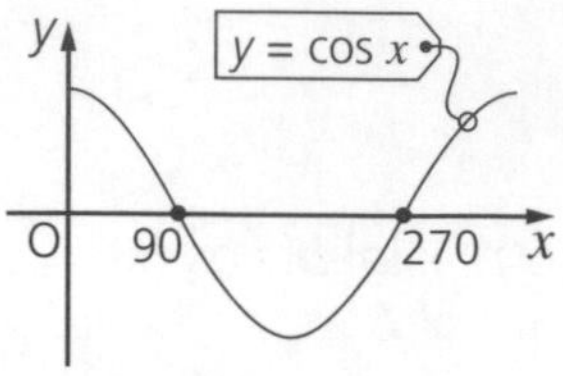

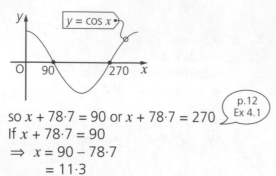

so $x + 78{\cdot}7 = 90$ or $x + 78{\cdot}7 = 270$

p.12 Ex 4.1

If $x + 78{\cdot}7 = 90$
$\Rightarrow x = 90 - 78{\cdot}7$
$= 11{\cdot}3$
This is not in the required range

If $x + 78{\cdot}7 = 270$
$\Rightarrow x = 270 - 78{\cdot}7$
$= 191{\cdot}3$
Thus $a = 191{\cdot}3$

8. a. Show that $\cos^2 x° - \cos 2x° = 1 - \cos^2 x°$
Left-hand side $= \cos^2 x° - \cos 2x°$
$= \cos^2 x° - (2\cos^2 x° - 1)$
$= \cos^2 x° - 2\cos^2 x° + 1$
$= 1 - \cos^2 x°$
= Right-hand side
so $\cos^2 x° - \cos 2x° = 1 - \cos^2 x°$

p.28 Ex 10.10

b. The equation $3\cos^2 x° - 3\cos 2x° = 8\cos x°$
becomes $3(\cos^2 x° - \cos 2x°) = 8\cos x°$
$\Rightarrow 3(1 - \cos^2 x°) = 8\cos x°$
(using part **a.**)
$\Rightarrow 3 - 3\cos^2 x° = 8\cos x°$
$\Rightarrow 3\cos^2 x° + 8\cos x° - 3 = 0$
$\Rightarrow (3\cos x° - 1)(\cos x° + 3) = 0$

so $3\cos x° - 1 = 0$ or $\cos x° + 3 = 0$

$\cos x° = \frac{1}{3}$ or $\cos x° = -3$

($x°$ is in 1st or 4th quadrants)

This equation has no solutions since $\cos x°$ is never less than -1.

so $x = 70{\cdot}5$ or $360 - 70{\cdot}5$
$= 289{\cdot}5$
$289{\cdot}5$ is not in the required range.

The only valid solution is $x = 70{\cdot}5$

p.27 Ex 10.6

9. $(kx + 2)(x + 3) = 8$
$kx^2 + 3kx + 2x + 6 = 8$
$kx^2 + (3k + 2)x - 2 = 0$
Discriminant $= (3k + 2)^2 - 4 \times k \times (-2)$
$= 9k^2 + 12k + 4 + 8k$
$= 9k^2 + 20k + 4$
For equal roots Discriminant = 0
so $9k^2 + 20k + 4 = 0$
$\Rightarrow (9k + 2)(k + 2) = 0$
$\Rightarrow 9k + 2 = 0$ or $k + 2 = 0$
$\Rightarrow k = -\frac{2}{9}$ or $k = -2$

p.21 Ex 8.4

10. a.

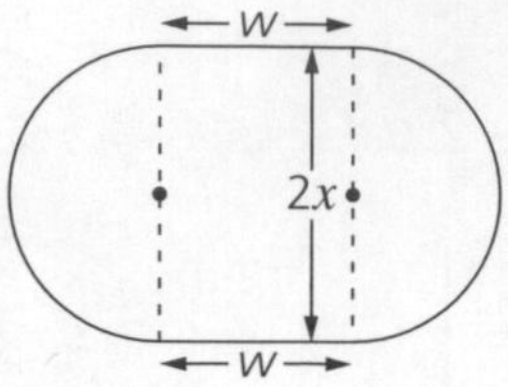

Two semi-circular arcs $= \pi \times 2x = 2\pi x$
Total perimeter $= 2\pi x + 2w$
So $2\pi x + 2w = 8$
$\Rightarrow 2w = 8 - 2\pi x$
$w = 4 - \pi x$

b. Area of clear glass (rectangle) $= w \times 2x$
$= (4 - \pi x) \times 2x$
$= 8x - 2\pi x^2$ m²
so light $= 3 \times (8x - 2\pi x^2)$
$= 24x - 6\pi x^2$ units
Area of frosted glass (a circle) $= \pi \times x^2$
(x is radius)
So light $= 2 \times \pi x^2 = 2\pi x^2$
Total light: $L = 24x - 6\pi x^2 + 2\pi x^2$
(clear) (frosted)

So $L = 24x - 4\pi x^2$

c. Method1

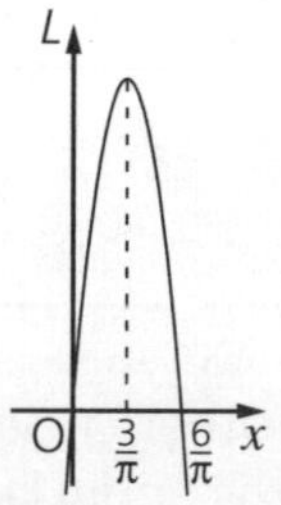

The graph of L against x is a parabola with a maximum turning point.
For x-axis intercept set $L = 0$
$\Rightarrow 24x - 4\pi x^2 = 0$
$\Rightarrow 4x(6 - \pi x) = 0$
$\Rightarrow x = 0$ or $x = \frac{6}{\pi}$

p.21 Ex 8.1

So the maximum value of L occurs when $x = \frac{3}{\pi}$ (midway between the x-axis intercepts)

When $x = \frac{3}{\pi}$, $w = 4 - \pi \times \frac{3}{\pi} = 4 - 3 = 1$

10. c. (cont.)

Method 2

Consider $L(x) = 24x - 4\pi x^2$

$L'(x) = 24 - 8\pi x$

For stationary points set $L'(x) = 0$

So $24 - 8\pi x = 0$

$\Rightarrow 8\pi x = 24$

$\Rightarrow x = \frac{24}{8\pi} = \frac{3}{\pi}$

and so $w = 4 - \pi \times \frac{3}{\pi} = 4 - 3 = 1$

The nature of the stationary point can be determined by a 'table of signs':

		$\frac{3}{\pi}$	
$L'(x)$	+		−
Shape of graph	/	−	\

So $x = \frac{3}{\pi}$ and $w = 1$ give the maximum value for L.

p.17 Ex 5.9

11. a. Using (1·649, 2·473) and (0, 0)

gives gradient $= \frac{2 \cdot 473}{1 \cdot 649} \doteqdot 1 \cdot 5$

The required equation is $Y = 1 \cdot 5X$

b. So $\log_e y = 1 \cdot 5 \log_e x$

$\Rightarrow \log_e y = \log_e x^{1 \cdot 5}$

$\Rightarrow y = x^{1 \cdot 5}$

Estimates are $a = 1$ and $b = 1 \cdot 5$

p.41 Ex 14.4

c. For Uranus $y = 84$ so $84 = x^{1 \cdot 5}$

Thus $\log_e 84 = \log_e x^{1 \cdot 5}$

$\Rightarrow \log_e 84 = 1 \cdot 5 \log_e x$

$\log_e x = \frac{\log_e 84}{1 \cdot 5} = 2 \cdot 953\ldots$

$\Rightarrow x = e^{2 \cdot 953\ldots}$

giving $x = 19 \cdot 18\ldots$

So $x \doteqdot 19 \cdot 2$ units (to 3 sig figs)

p.40 Ex 14.2

SOLUTIONS TO PRACTICE EXAM B

Each (speech bubble) refers back to an exercise which practises the skill or technique occurring in the solution at that point. Use these references to identify your weaknesses and use the corresponding exercises to practise those skills.

SOLUTIONS TO EXAM B PAPER 1

1. a. For A(1, 2) and B(−3, −1) then

$AB = \sqrt{(1-(-3))^2 + (2-(-1))^2}$

$= \sqrt{16+9} = \sqrt{25} = 5$

For A(1, 2) and C(4, −2) then

$AC = \sqrt{(1-4)^2 + (2-(-2))^2}$

$= \sqrt{9+16} = \sqrt{25} = 5$

so AB = AC

and triangle ABC is isosceles

p.7 Ex 1.10

b. $m_{AB} = \frac{2-(-1)}{1-(-3)} = \frac{3}{4}$

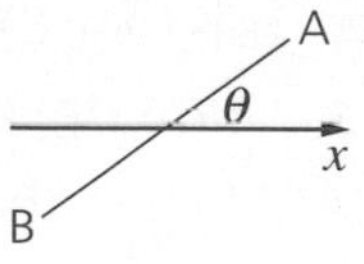

$\tan\theta = \frac{3}{4}$

p.5 Ex 1.2

2. $f(x) = 2x^2$ and $g(x) = 4 - x^2$

a. $g(f(x)) = g(2x^2) = 4 - (2x^2)^2$

$= 4 - 4x^4$

p.10 Ex 3.4

b. $4 - 4x^4 = 4(1 - x^4)$

$= 4(1 - x^2)(1 + x^2)$

$= 4(1 - x)(1 + x)(1 + x^2)$

3. Let $y = \frac{2x+6}{\sqrt{x}} = \frac{2x+6}{x^{\frac{1}{2}}} = \frac{2x^1}{x^{\frac{1}{2}}} + \frac{6}{x^{\frac{1}{2}}} = 2x^{\frac{1}{2}} + 6x^{-\frac{1}{2}}$

So $\frac{dy}{dx} = \frac{1}{2} \times 2x^{-\frac{1}{2}} - \frac{1}{2} \times 6x^{-\frac{3}{2}}$

$= x^{-\frac{1}{2}} - 3x^{-\frac{3}{2}}$

p.14–15 Ex 5.2 Ex 5.3

4. a. A limit exists since the multiplier $\frac{7}{10}$ lies between −1 and 1.

p.19 Ex 6.2

b. Let the limit of this sequence be L.

Then $L = \frac{7}{10}L + 2 \Rightarrow L - \frac{7}{10}L = 2$

$\Rightarrow \frac{3}{10}L = 2 \Rightarrow 3L = 20$

$\Rightarrow L = \frac{20}{3} = 6\frac{2}{3}$

p.19 Ex 6.3

c. Let the new multiplier be x. Since L = 7 this gives $7 = x \times 7 + 2$

(L replaced by 7 and $\frac{7}{10}$ replaced by x)

$\Rightarrow 7 = 7x + 2 \Rightarrow 7x = 5 \Rightarrow x = \frac{5}{7}$

The new multiplier is $\frac{5}{7}$

5. a. A$(\frac{\pi}{6}, a)$ lies on $y = \sin x$.

When $x = \frac{\pi}{6}$ and $y = a$, this gives

$a = \sin\frac{\pi}{6} = \frac{1}{2}$ (exact value).

B$(\frac{\pi}{2}, b)$ lies on $y = \sin x$.

When $x = \frac{\pi}{2}$ and $y = b$, then $b = \sin\frac{\pi}{2} = 1$

So $a = \frac{1}{2}$ and $b = 1$

p.12 Ex 4.2

b. $\int_{\frac{\pi}{6}}^{\frac{\pi}{2}} \sin x\,dx = \left[-\cos x\right]_{\frac{\pi}{6}}^{\frac{\pi}{2}}$

$= (-\cos\frac{\pi}{2}) - (-\cos\frac{\pi}{6})$

$= -0 + \frac{\sqrt{3}}{2} = \frac{\sqrt{3}}{2}$

Area of the shaded region

is $\frac{\sqrt{3}}{2}$ unit²

p.37 Ex 13.2

6. a.

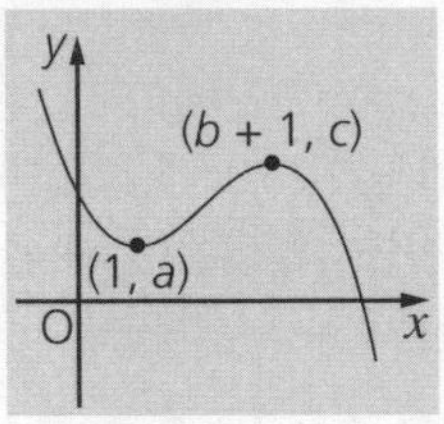

The original graph moves 1 unit right parallel to the x-axis.

p.9 Ex 3.3

b. Differentiating a cubic expression produces a quadratic expression. So $y = f'(x)$ is a parabola. Stationary points occur when $x = 0$ and $x = b$ ($f'(0) = 0$ and $f'(b) = 0$) i.e. $y = f'(x)$ intersects the axis for these values of x:

Sketch of $y = f'(x)$

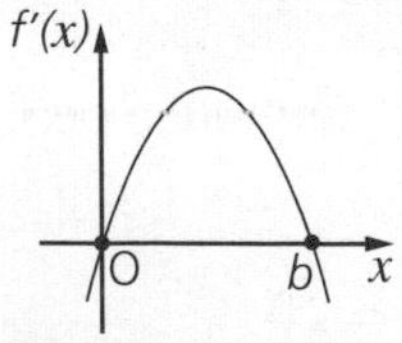

p.16 Ex 5.5

7. $2y - 3x = 6 \Rightarrow 2y = 3x + 6 \Rightarrow y = \frac{3}{2}x + 3$

The gradient of this line is $\frac{3}{2}$

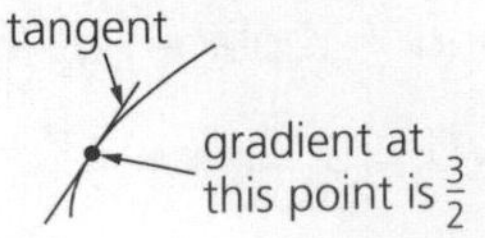

$y = 2\sqrt{x+1} = 2(x+1)^{\frac{1}{2}}$

$\Rightarrow \frac{dy}{dx} = \frac{1}{2} \times 2(x+1)^{-\frac{1}{2}} \times 1$

$= (x+1)^{-\frac{1}{2}} = \frac{1}{\sqrt{(x+1)}}$

This is the gradient formula for the curve.

7. (cont.) So for $\frac{dy}{dx} = \frac{3}{2} \Rightarrow \frac{1}{\sqrt{(x+1)}} = \frac{3}{2}$

$\Rightarrow 2 = 3\sqrt{(x+1)}$

$\Rightarrow 4 = 9 \times (x + 1)$ (after squaring both sides)

$\Rightarrow x + 1 = \frac{4}{9}$

$\Rightarrow x = \frac{4}{9} - 1 = -\frac{5}{9}$

p.17 Ex 5.7

8. For point of intersection solve:

$$\left.\begin{array}{l} y = kx(3-x) \\ y = x+1 \end{array}\right\} \Rightarrow kx(3 - x) = x + 1$$

$\Rightarrow 3kx - kx^2 = x + 1$

$\Rightarrow kx^2 + x - 3kx + 1 = 0$

$\Rightarrow kx^2 + (1 - 3k)x + 1 = 0$

Discriminant $= (1 - 3k)^2 - 4 \times k \times 1$
$= 1 - 6k + 9k^2 - 4k$
$= 9k^2 - 10k + 1$

Since $y = x + 1$ is a tangent there is only one point of contact, i.e. only one solution to the quadratic equation, i.e. the Discriminant = 0
So $9k^2 - 10k + 1 = 0 \Rightarrow (9k - 1)(k - 1) = 0$
$\Rightarrow k = \frac{1}{9}$ or $k = 1$
Since k is a positive integer ($\frac{1}{9}$ is not) then $k = 1$ is the only solution.

p.21 Ex 8.4

9. a. Left-hand side
$= (\sin A + \cos B)^2 + (\cos A + \sin B)^2$

$= \sin^2 A + 2\sin A \cos B + \cos^2 B + \cos^2 A + 2\cos A \sin B + \sin^2 B$

$= (\sin^2 A + \cos^2 A) + (\sin^2 B + \cos^2 B) + 2(\sin A \cos B + \cos A \sin B)$

$= 1 + 1 + 2\sin(A + B)$

$= 2 + 2\sin(A + B)$

= Right-hand side

p.28 Ex 10.10

b. The equation
$(\sin A + \cos B)^2 + (\cos A + \sin B)^2 = 3$
becomes $2 + 2\sin(A + B) = 3$
$\Rightarrow 2\sin(A + B) = 1$
$\Rightarrow \sin(A + B) = \frac{1}{2}$
[(A + B) is in the 1st or 2nd quadrants and

1st quadrant angle is $\frac{\pi}{6}$]

So $(A + B) = \frac{\pi}{6}$ or $\pi - \frac{\pi}{6} = \frac{5\pi}{6}$

p.26 Ex 10.4

10.

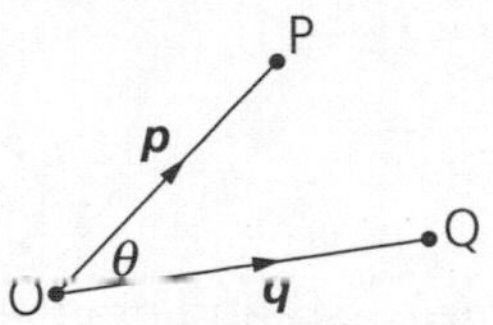

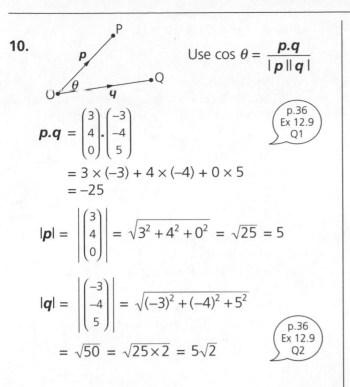

Use $\cos\theta = \dfrac{\boldsymbol{p}.\boldsymbol{q}}{|\boldsymbol{p}||\boldsymbol{q}|}$

p.36 Ex 12.9 Q1

$$\boldsymbol{p}.\boldsymbol{q} = \begin{pmatrix}3\\4\\0\end{pmatrix}.\begin{pmatrix}-3\\-4\\5\end{pmatrix}$$

$= 3\times(-3) + 4\times(-4) + 0\times5$
$= -25$

$$|\boldsymbol{p}| = \left|\begin{pmatrix}3\\4\\0\end{pmatrix}\right| = \sqrt{3^2+4^2+0^2} = \sqrt{25} = 5$$

$$|\boldsymbol{q}| = \left|\begin{pmatrix}-3\\-4\\5\end{pmatrix}\right| = \sqrt{(-3)^2+(-4)^2+5^2}$$

$= \sqrt{50} = \sqrt{25\times2} = 5\sqrt{2}$

p.36 Ex 12.9 Q2

10. (cont.) So $\cos\theta = \dfrac{-25}{5\times5\sqrt{2}} = -\dfrac{1}{\sqrt{2}}$

(θ is in 2nd quadrant since $0 \le \theta \le \pi$)

(1st quadrant angle is $\frac{\pi}{4}$)

$\Rightarrow \ \theta = \pi - \frac{\pi}{4} = \frac{3\pi}{4}$ So $\angle POQ = \frac{3\pi}{4}$

p.35 Ex 12.6

($180° - 45° = 135°$ is acceptable)

11.

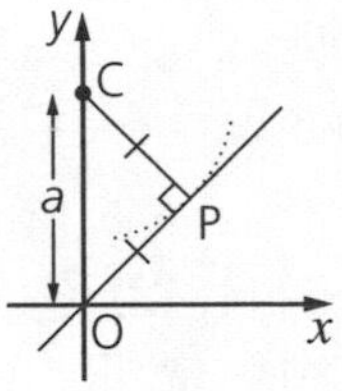

Triangle CPO is isosceles with CP = OP = 2
So $a^2 = 2^2 + 2^2 = 8$

$a = \sqrt{8} = 2\sqrt{2}$

p.31 Ex 11.1 Q1

Required equation is
$(x-a)^2 + (y-0)^2 = 2^2$

i.e. $(x - 2\sqrt{2})^2 + y^2 = 4$

p.31 Ex 11.4

SOLUTIONS TO EXAM B PAPER 2

1. a. $\boldsymbol{a} = \begin{pmatrix}p\\0\\-1\end{pmatrix}$ and $\boldsymbol{b} = \begin{pmatrix}2\\1\\1\end{pmatrix} \Rightarrow \boldsymbol{a}.\boldsymbol{b} = \begin{pmatrix}p\\0\\-1\end{pmatrix}.\begin{pmatrix}2\\1\\1\end{pmatrix}$

$= p\times2 + 0\times1 + (-1)\times1$
$= 2p - 1$

Since $\boldsymbol{a}$ and $\boldsymbol{b}$ are perpendicular
then $\boldsymbol{a}.\boldsymbol{b} = 0$
So $2p - 1 = 0 \Rightarrow 2p = 1$
$\Rightarrow p = \frac{1}{2}$

p.35 Ex 12.7

b. $|\boldsymbol{a}| = \left|\begin{pmatrix}\frac{1}{2}\\0\\-1\end{pmatrix}\right| = \sqrt{\left(\frac{1}{2}\right)^2 + 0^2 + (-1)^2}$

$= \sqrt{\frac{1}{4}+1} = \sqrt{\frac{5}{4}} = \frac{\sqrt{5}}{2}$

$|2\boldsymbol{a} - \boldsymbol{b}| = \left|2\begin{pmatrix}\frac{1}{2}\\0\\-1\end{pmatrix} - \begin{pmatrix}2\\1\\1\end{pmatrix}\right| = \left|\begin{pmatrix}-1\\-1\\-3\end{pmatrix}\right|$

$= \sqrt{(-1)^2 + (-1)^2 + (-3)^2}$

$= \sqrt{11}$

p.33 Ex 12.2

1. c. $\boldsymbol{a}.(2\boldsymbol{a} - \boldsymbol{b}) = \begin{pmatrix}\frac{1}{2}\\0\\-1\end{pmatrix}.\begin{pmatrix}-1\\-1\\-3\end{pmatrix}$

$= \frac{1}{2}\times(-1) + 0\times(-1) + (-1)\times(-3)$

$= \frac{5}{2}$

d.

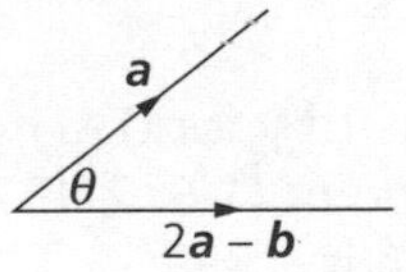

Use $\cos\theta = \dfrac{\boldsymbol{a}.(2\boldsymbol{a}-\boldsymbol{b})}{|\boldsymbol{a}||2\boldsymbol{a}-\boldsymbol{b}|}$

$= \dfrac{\frac{5}{2}}{\frac{\sqrt{5}}{2}\times\sqrt{11}}$ $\begin{matrix}(\times 2\sqrt{5})\\(\times 2\sqrt{5})\end{matrix}$

$= \dfrac{5\sqrt{5}}{5\sqrt{11}} = \sqrt{\frac{5}{11}} = 0{\cdot}674\ldots$

giving $\theta \doteqdot 47{\cdot}6°$

p.35 Ex 12.6

2. a. $y = 3 + 2x^2 - x^4 \Rightarrow \frac{dy}{dx} = 4x - 4x^3$

For stationary points set $\frac{dy}{dx} = 0$
so $4x - 4x^3 = 0 \Rightarrow 4x(1 - x^2) = 0$
$\Rightarrow 4x(1 - x)(1 + x) = 0$
$\Rightarrow x = 0$ or $x = 1$ or $x = -1$
When $x = 0$, $y = 3 + 2 \times 0^2 - 0^4 = 3$
giving (0, 3)
When $x = 1$, $y = 3 + 2 \times 1^2 - 1^4 = 4$
giving (1, 4)
When $x = -1$, $y = 3 + 2 \times (-1)^2 - (-1)^4 = 4$
giving (–1, 4)

The stationary points are (–1, 4), (0, 3) and (1, 4)

b.

		−1		0		1	
$\frac{dy}{dx} = 4x(1-x)(1+x)$	+		−		+		−

Shape of graph: 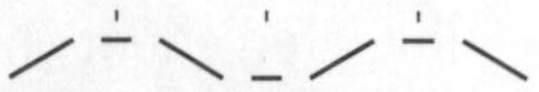

So (–1, 4) and (1, 4) are maximum stationary points and (0, 3) is a minimum stationary point.

p.17 Ex 5.9

c. When $x = 1{\cdot}5$
$y = 3 + 2 \times 1{\cdot}5^2 - 1{\cdot}5^4 = 2{\cdot}4375$

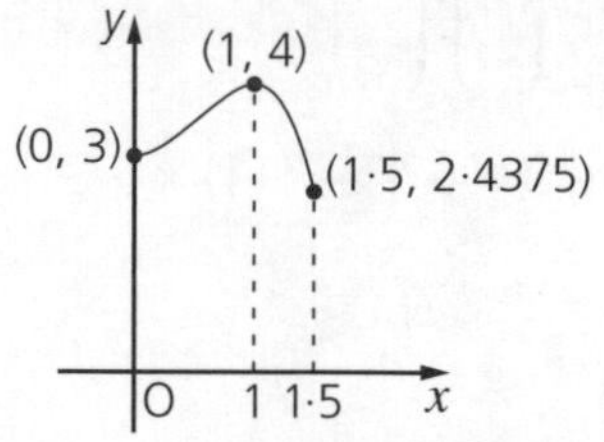

The minimum value of y for $0 \leq x \leq 1{\cdot}5$ occurs at the end point (1·5, 2·4375).
The minimum value is 2·4375.

3. a. The minimum value of $(x - b)^2$ is 0^2
so the minimum value of $a(x - b)^2 + c$ is $a \times 0^2 + c = c$ and this occurs when $x = b$.
Since (6, 8) is the minimum turning point
Then $b = 6$ and $c = 8$

p.11 Ex 3.7

b. $y = a(x - 6)^2 + 8$
$\Rightarrow \frac{dy}{dx} = 2a(x - 6)$

when $x = 5$, $\frac{dy}{dx} = -1$
So $2a(5 - 6) = -1$
$\Rightarrow -2a = -1$
$\Rightarrow a = \frac{1}{2}$

4. a. $x^2 + y^2 + 4x + 2y - 15 = 0$

Centre: (–2, –1)

p.31 Ex 11.2

So point on AB is (–2, –1) and gradient is 2
equation of AB is $y - (-1) = 2(x - (-2))$
$\Rightarrow y + 1 = 2(x + 2)$
$\Rightarrow y = 2x + 3$

p.6 Ex 1.7

The line AB, with equation $y = 2x + 3$, has y-axis intercept of (0, 3)

p.6 Ex 1.8

when $x = 0$ and $y = 3$
$x^2 + y^2 + 4x + 2y - 15$
$= 0^2 + 3^2 + 4 \times 0 + 2 \times 3 - 15$
$= 0$
So (0, 3) also lies on the circle. Hence A(0, 3) is the point of intersection of the line and circle and lies on the y-axis.

b.

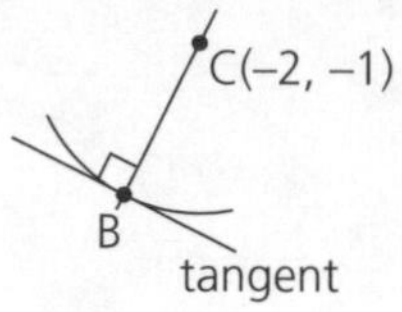

now $\overrightarrow{AC} = \overrightarrow{CB}$
So $\mathbf{c} - \mathbf{a} = \mathbf{b} - \mathbf{c}$
$\mathbf{b} = 2\mathbf{c} - \mathbf{a}$
$= 2\begin{pmatrix}-2\\-1\end{pmatrix} - \begin{pmatrix}0\\3\end{pmatrix}$
$= \begin{pmatrix}-4\\-5\end{pmatrix}$

Thus B(–4, –5)

So $m_{BC} = \frac{-1 - (-5)}{-2 - (-4)} = \frac{4}{2} = 2 \Rightarrow m_{\perp} = -\frac{1}{2}$

gradient of tangent is $-\frac{1}{2}$, point on tangent is B(–4, –5)
so equation of tangent is
$y - (-5) = -\frac{1}{2}(x - (-4))$
$\Rightarrow y + 5 = -\frac{1}{2}(x + 4)$
$\Rightarrow 2y + 10 = -x - 4$
$\Rightarrow 2y + x = -14$

p.32 Ex 11.6 Q1, Q2

5.

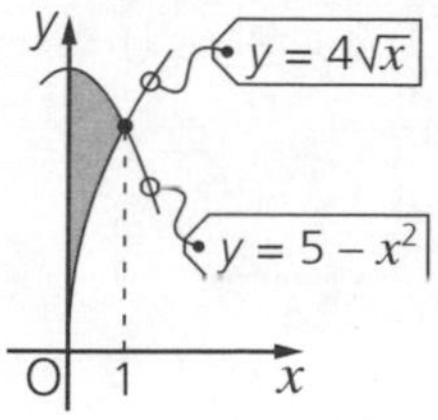

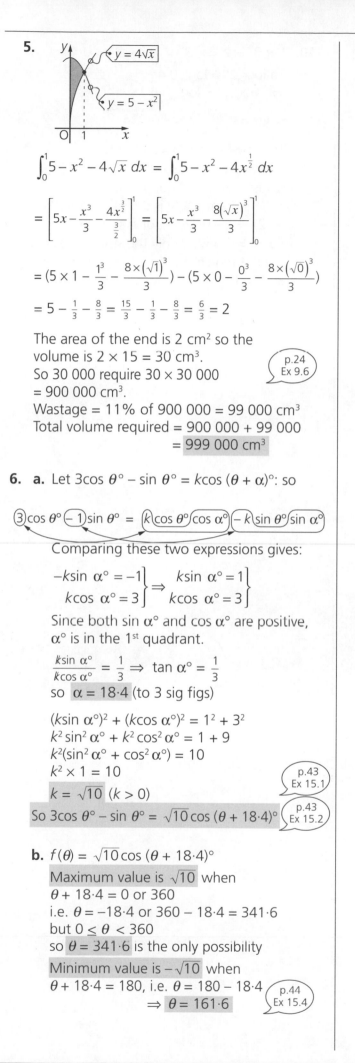

$$\int_0^1 5 - x^2 - 4\sqrt{x}\,dx = \int_0^1 5 - x^2 - 4x^{\frac{1}{2}}\,dx$$

$$= \left[5x - \frac{x^3}{3} - \frac{4x^{\frac{3}{2}}}{\frac{3}{2}}\right]_0^1 = \left[5x - \frac{x^3}{3} - \frac{8(\sqrt{x})^3}{3}\right]_0^1$$

$$= (5 \times 1 - \frac{1^3}{3} - \frac{8 \times (\sqrt{1})^3}{3}) - (5 \times 0 - \frac{0^3}{3} - \frac{8 \times (\sqrt{0})^3}{3})$$

$$= 5 - \tfrac{1}{3} - \tfrac{8}{3} = \tfrac{15}{3} - \tfrac{1}{3} - \tfrac{8}{3} = \tfrac{6}{3} = 2$$

The area of the end is 2 cm^2 so the volume is $2 \times 15 = 30$ cm^3.
So 30 000 require $30 \times 30\,000$
$= 900\,000$ cm^3.
Wastage = 11% of 900 000 = 99 000 cm^3
Total volume required = 900 000 + 99 000
= 999 000 cm^3

p.24 Ex 9.6

6. a. Let $3\cos\theta° - \sin\theta° = k\cos(\theta + \alpha)°$: so

$$3\cos\theta° - 1\sin\theta° = k\cos\theta°\cos\alpha° - k\sin\theta°\sin\alpha°$$

Comparing these two expressions gives:

$$\left.\begin{array}{r}-k\sin\alpha° = -1\\ k\cos\alpha° = 3\end{array}\right\} \Rightarrow \left.\begin{array}{r}k\sin\alpha° = 1\\ k\cos\alpha° = 3\end{array}\right\}$$

Since both $\sin\alpha°$ and $\cos\alpha°$ are positive, $\alpha°$ is in the 1st quadrant.

$$\frac{k\sin\alpha°}{k\cos\alpha°} = \frac{1}{3} \Rightarrow \tan\alpha° = \frac{1}{3}$$

so $\alpha = 18{\cdot}4$ (to 3 sig figs)

$(k\sin\alpha°)^2 + (k\cos\alpha°)^2 = 1^2 + 3^2$
$k^2\sin^2\alpha° + k^2\cos^2\alpha° = 1 + 9$
$k^2(\sin^2\alpha° + \cos^2\alpha°) = 10$
$k^2 \times 1 = 10$
$k = \sqrt{10}$ $(k > 0)$

p.43 Ex 15.1

So $3\cos\theta° - \sin\theta° = \sqrt{10}\cos(\theta + 18{\cdot}4)°$

p.43 Ex 15.2

b. $f(\theta) = \sqrt{10}\cos(\theta + 18{\cdot}4)°$
Maximum value is $\sqrt{10}$ when
$\theta + 18{\cdot}4 = 0$ or 360
i.e. $\theta = -18{\cdot}4$ or $360 - 18{\cdot}4 = 341{\cdot}6$
but $0 \leq \theta < 360$
so $\theta = 341{\cdot}6$ is the only possibility
Minimum value is $-\sqrt{10}$ when
$\theta + 18{\cdot}4 = 180$, i.e. $\theta = 180 - 18{\cdot}4$
$\Rightarrow \theta = 161{\cdot}6$

p.44 Ex 15.4

6. c. $\sqrt{10}(3\cos\theta° - \sin\theta°) + 10$
$= \sqrt{10} \times \sqrt{10}\cos(\theta + 18{\cdot}4)° + 10$
So minimum value is $\sqrt{10} \times \sqrt{10} \times (-1) + 10$
$= -10 + 10 = 0$

7. a. Since x and y obey an allometric law then $y = ax^b$
$\Rightarrow \log_e y = \log_e(ax^b)$
$\Rightarrow \log_e y = \log_e a + \log_e(x^b)$
$\Rightarrow \log_e y = \log_e a + b\log_e x$
$\Rightarrow \log_e y = b\log_e x + \log_e a$
(compare $Y = m\ \ X\ +\ c$)

and so there is a linear relationship between $\log_e y$ and $\log_e x$

b.

x	31·9	138·7
y	78·5	122·0

→

$\log_e x$	3·463	4·932
$\log_e y$	4·363	4·804

This gives
$$\left.\begin{array}{l}4{\cdot}363 = b \times 3{\cdot}463 + \log_e a\\ 4{\cdot}804 = b \times 4{\cdot}932 + \log_e a\end{array}\right\}$$

$\Rightarrow 4{\cdot}804 - 4{\cdot}363 = b(4{\cdot}932 - 3{\cdot}463)$

$\Rightarrow b = \dfrac{4{\cdot}804 - 4{\cdot}363}{4{\cdot}932 - 3{\cdot}463}$

(gradient of linear graph)
$\Rightarrow b \doteqdot 0{\cdot}300$ (to 3 sig figs)
So $4{\cdot}363 = 0{\cdot}3 \times 3{\cdot}463 + \log_e a$
$\Rightarrow \log_e a = 4{\cdot}363 - 0{\cdot}3 \times 3{\cdot}463$
$= 3{\cdot}324$
$a = e^{3{\cdot}324} \doteqdot 27{\cdot}8$ (to 3 sig figs)

p.41 Ex 14.4

8. a. $f(x) = x^4 + 4x^3 + 5x^2 + 14x + 24$

−2	1	4	5	14	24
		−2	−4	−2	−24
	1	2	1	12	0

So $f(x) = (x + 2)(x^3 + 2x^2 + x + 12)$

−3	1	2	1	12
		−3	3	−12
	1	−1	4	0

giving $f(x) = (x + 2)(x + 3)(x^2 - x + 4)$

Thus $a = 2$ and $b = 3$
(or $a = 3$ and $b = 2$)

p.20 Ex 7.2

b. The equation $f(x) = 0$ becomes
$(x + 2)(x + 3)(x^2 - x + 4) = 0$
So $x + 2 = 0$ or $x + 3 = 0$ or $x^2 - x + 4 = 0$
$\Rightarrow x = -2$ or $x = -3$
For $x^2 - x + 4 = 0$
the discriminant $= (-1)^2 - 4 \times 1 \times 4$
$= 1 - 16 = -15$
Since this is negative there are no real roots.

p.21 Ex 8.2

The only two real roots of $f(x) = 0$ are
$x = -2$ and $x = -3$

9. a. These two triangles are similar:

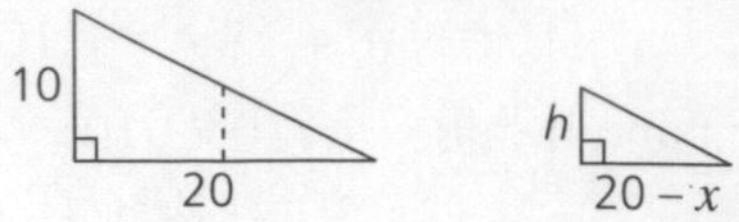

base = 2 × height so $20 - x = 2h$

Thus $h = \frac{1}{2}(20 - x)$

$\Rightarrow h = 10 - \frac{1}{2}x$

b.

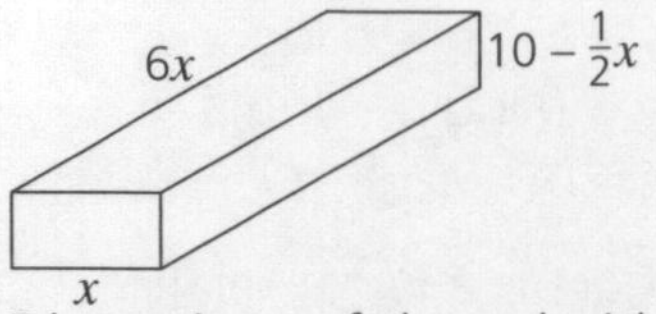

Dimensions of the cuboid are

x cm × $6x$ cm × $(10 - \frac{1}{2}x)$ cm

So $V(x) = x \times 6x \times (10 - \frac{1}{2}x)$

$= 6x^2(10 - \frac{1}{2}x)$

$= 60x^2 - 3x^3$

c. $V'(x) = 120x - 9x^2$

For stationary points set $V'(x) = 0$

So $120x - 9x^2 = 0 \Rightarrow 3x(40 - 3x) = 0$

$\Rightarrow x = 0$ or $x = \frac{40}{3}$ ($x = 0$ will not give a maximum volume!)

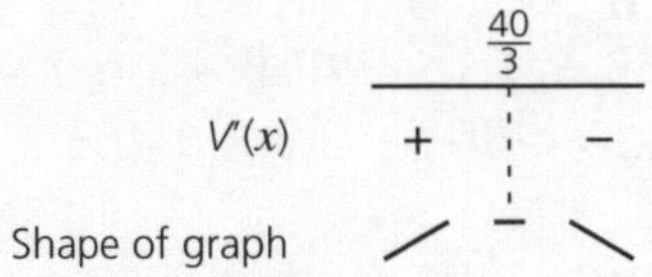

Thus $x = \frac{40}{3}$ gives a maximum volume.

p.17
Ex 5.9

In this case $6x = 6 \times \frac{40}{3} = 80$

and $10 - \frac{1}{2}x = 10 - \frac{1}{2} \times \frac{40}{3} = 10 - \frac{20}{3} = \frac{10}{3}$

The required dimensions are:

$\frac{40}{3}$ cm × 80 cm × $\frac{10}{3}$ cm

10. $5 \times 3^{\alpha} = 2 \Rightarrow 3^{\alpha} = \frac{2}{5} \Rightarrow 3^{\alpha} = 0{\cdot}4$

So $\log_{10}3^{\alpha} = \log_{10}0{\cdot}4$

$\Rightarrow \alpha\log_{10}3 = \log_{10}0{\cdot}4$

$\Rightarrow \alpha = \frac{\log_{10}0{\cdot}4}{\log_{10}3} = -0{\cdot}834\ldots$

p.40
Ex 14.2
Q4

Thus $\cos^2 x - \sin^2 x = -0{\cdot}834\ldots$

$\Rightarrow \cos 2x = -0{\cdot}834\ldots$

($2x$ is in 2nd or 3rd quadrants)

(1st quadrant angle is $0{\cdot}584\ldots$ **radians**)

So $2x = \pi - 0{\cdot}584\ldots$ or $\pi + 0{\cdot}584\ldots$

So $2x = 2{\cdot}557\ldots$ only the smallest positive value is required.

So $x = 1{\cdot}278\ldots$

The required value is:

$x \doteqdot 1{\cdot}28$ (to 3 sig figs)

p.26
Ex 10.5

Exercise 10.11 Triangle problems

1. For each diagram find the exact value of **(i)** $\sin\left(\frac{x}{2}\right)^\circ$ **(ii)** $\cos\left(\frac{x}{2}\right)^\circ$

a.

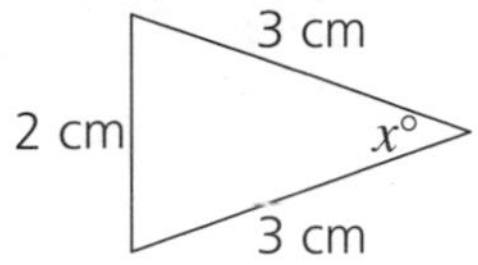

b.

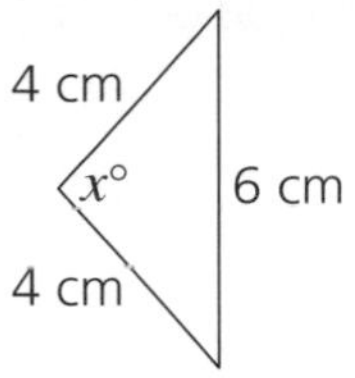

c.

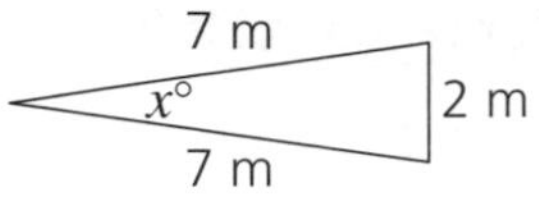

d.

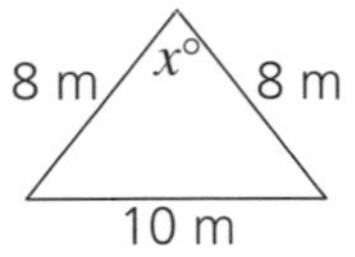

e.

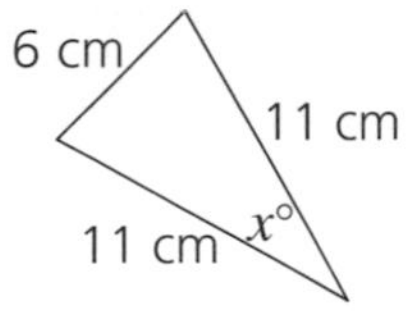

Hint: Draw the altitude that is the axis of symmetry.

2. In each case find the exact value of $\sin x^\circ$:

a.

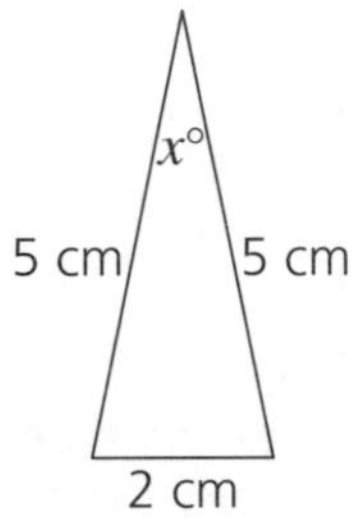

b.

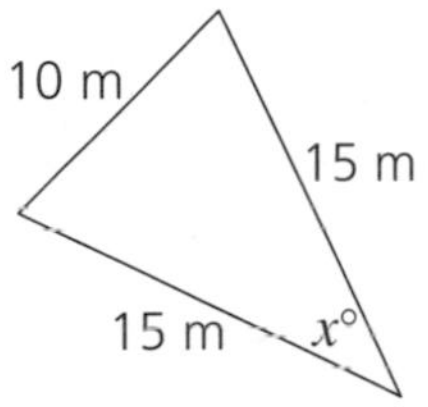

c.

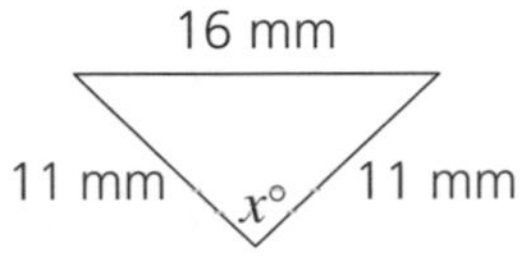

Hint: Rewrite $\sin x^\circ$ using the Double Angle Formula.
(See Exercise 10.9 above.)

3. A billboard is supported by a wooden support wedge as shown in the diagram. The wedge has dimensions as shown in the diagram on the right.

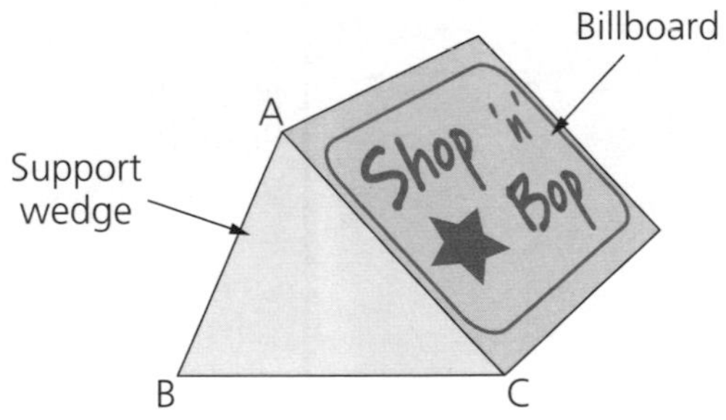

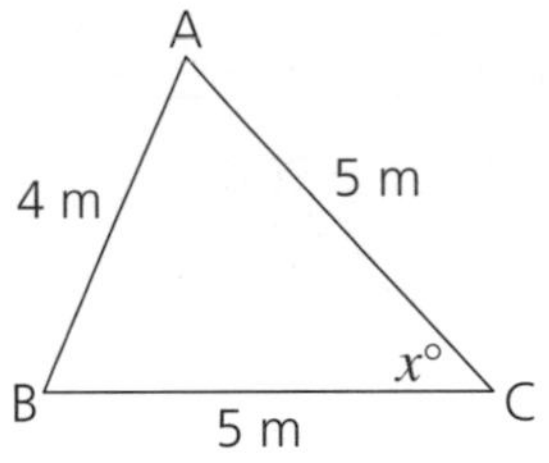

Find the exact value of $\sin x^\circ$ where x° is the angle at which the billboard is inclined to the horizontal.

Exercise 10.12 Equation solving using Double Angle Formulae

1. Find values for $\sin x^\circ$ and/or $\cos x^\circ$:

a. $\sin 2x^\circ = 0$ **b.** $\sin 2x^\circ - \sin x^\circ = 0$ **c.** $\cos x^\circ + \sin 2x^\circ = 0$

d. $\sin 2x^\circ - \cos x^\circ = 0$ **e.** $\sin 2x^\circ + 2\sin x^\circ = 0$ **f.** $\cos x^\circ - 2\sin 2x^\circ = 0$

See these pages in Leckie & Leckie's *Higher Maths Course Notes:*

page 37.
A similar calculation is done in example 10.9.
(1st ed: page 37, example 10.8)

2. Solve:

a. $\sin 2x^\circ - \sin x^\circ = 0$ for $0 \le x \le 360$

b. $\cos x + \sin 2x = 0$ for $0 \le x \le 2\pi$

c. $\sin 2x^\circ - \cos x^\circ = 0$ for $0 \le x \le 360$

d. $\sin 2x + 2\sin x = 0$ for $0 \le x < 2\pi$

e. $2\cos x^\circ - 2\sin 2x^\circ = 0$ for $0 \le x < 360$

f. $2\sin x^\circ + 3\sin 2x^\circ = 0$ for $0 \le x < 360$

g. $\sqrt{2}\sin 2x + 2\cos x = 0$ for $0 \le x \le 2\pi$

h. $\sqrt{3}\sin 2x + 3\sin x = 0$ for $\pi \le x \le 2\pi$

3. In each case choose the appropriate substitution for $\cos 2x$ and then rearrange into 'normal' quadratic equation order.

a. $\cos 2x - \cos x = 0$

b. $\cos 2x + \sin x = 0$

c. $\sin x - \cos 2x = 0$

d. $2 + \cos 2x - \cos x = 0$

e. $\cos 2x + 1 = \cos x$

f. $\cos 2x = \sin x + 1$

g. $3 - 2\cos 2x = 3\cos x + 4$

h. $3\cos 2x - 2\sin x + 1 = 0$

4. Solve:

a. $\cos 2x - \cos x = 0$ for $0 \le x \le 2\pi$

b. $\cos 2x^\circ + \sin x^\circ = 0$ for $0 \le x \le 360$

c. $\cos 2x^\circ - \sin x^\circ = 0$ for $0 \le x \le 360$

d. $\cos 2x + \cos x + 1 = 0$ for $0 \le x \le 2\pi$

e. $\cos 2x^\circ - \sin x^\circ - 1 = 0$ for $0 \le x \le 360$

f. $3\sin x + 2 = \cos 2x$ for $0 \le x \le 2\pi$

g. $4\cos 2x^\circ = 2\sin x^\circ + 1$ for $0 \le x \le 360$

h. $\cos x^\circ - 5\cos 2x^\circ = 2$ for $0 \le x \le 360$

See these pages in Leckie & Leckie's *Higher Maths Course Notes:*

Page 37, example 10.9 should help (1st ed: page 37, example 10.8).

page 37. See the example at the top of the page.

Exercise 11.1 Equations using centre and radius

1. Find the equation of the circle with the given centre and radius.

a. (2, 4); 6 **b.** (–1, 3); 5 **c.** (2, –3); 2 **d.** (–3, –4); 1
e. (0, –4); 2 **f.** (–2, 0); 5 **g.** (–3, 7); $\sqrt{3}$ **h.** (10, –1); $\sqrt{17}$

2. Find the equation of the circle that has P and Q as the end points of a diameter.

a. P(2, 3) and Q(8, 1) **b.** P(–1, 2) and Q(11, 18)
c. P(2, 1) and Q(–6, –5) **d.** P(–7, –2) and Q(3, 18)
e. P(0, –1) and Q(2, –3) **f.** P(3, –8) and Q(–1, 0)
g. P($\frac{1}{2}$, $-\frac{1}{2}$) and Q($\frac{3}{2}$, $-\frac{3}{2}$) **h.** P($\frac{1}{2}$, $-\frac{1}{2}$) and Q($-\frac{1}{2}$, $\frac{3}{2}$)

Hint: The centre is the midpoint of the diameter.

Exercise 11.2 The General Equation

Find the centre and radius of each circle:

1. $x^2 + y^2 - 2x + 4y + 1 = 0$ **2.** $x^2 + y^2 + 6x - 2y + 1 = 0$
3. $x^2 + y^2 + 4x - 2y - 4 = 0$ **4.** $x^2 + y^2 + 10x - 6y - 2 = 0$
5. $x^2 + y^2 - 8x - 8y + 7 = 0$ **6.** $x^2 + y^2 - x - y - \frac{1}{2} = 0$
7. $x^2 + y^2 - 6x + 8y = 0$ **8.** $2x^2 + 2y^2 - 20y - 22 = 0$

Exercise 11.3 The radius is positive

The following represent circles. Find the possible range of values of k:

1. $x^2 + y^2 + 2x - 4y - k = 0$ **2.** $x^2 + y^2 + 2y + k = 0$
3. $x^2 + y^2 - 6x + k = 0$ **4.** $x^2 + y^2 - x - y - k = 0$
5. $x^2 + y^2 + 2kx - 8y + 25 = 0$ **6.** $x^2 + y^2 + kx + ky + 2 = 0$

Exercise 11.4 Problem solving

In each question use the information given to find the equation of the circle:

1. A circle passes through the origin and the point (30, 0) and has the line $y = -5$ as a tangent.

2. The line $y = 2$ is a tangent to a circle which passes through (0, 0) and (12, 0).

3. A circle which passes through the origin and has the line $x = -1$ as a tangent also passes through the point (0, 10).

4. A circle passing through (–8, 0) and (8, 0) has the line $y = 2$ as a tangent.

5. The line $y = 1$ is a tangent to a circle which passes through (–1, 0) and (5, 0).

6. A circle with $x = 1$ as a tangent passes through points (0, 1) and (0, 7).

See these pages in Leckie & Leckie's *Higher Maths Course Notes:*

page 39. The first part of example 11.1 is useful.

page 39, example 11.2

page 39, example 11.3

Exercise 11.5 Proving lines are tangents

See these pages in Leckie & Leckie's *Higher Maths Course Notes:*

page 40, example 11.4

In each case show that the line is a tangent to the circle and find the point of contact.

1. $y = 2 - x$ and $x^2 + y^2 = 2$
2. $y = x - 1$ and $x^2 + y^2 + 2x - 1 = 0$
3. $y + x + 1 = 0$ and $x^2 + y^2 - 4x + 2y + 3 = 0$
4. $y - x = 5$ and $x^2 + y^2 + 6x + 4y + 5 = 0$

Exercise 11.6 Finding equations of tangents

1. Find the gradient of the tangent at P:

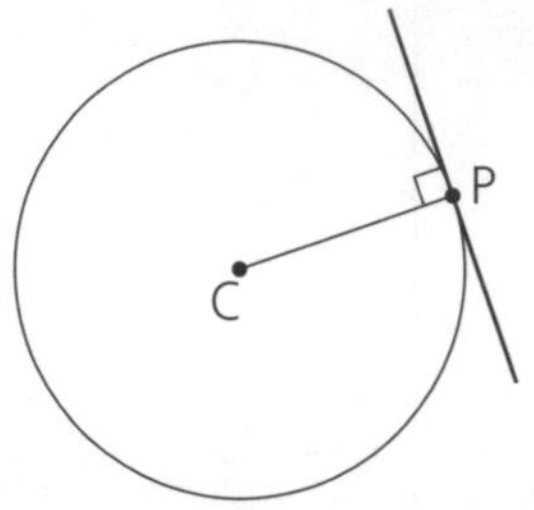

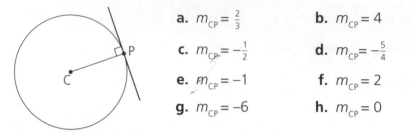

a. $m_{CP} = \frac{2}{3}$ **b.** $m_{CP} = 4$

c. $m_{CP} = -\frac{1}{2}$ **d.** $m_{CP} = -\frac{5}{4}$

e. $m_{CP} = -1$ **f.** $m_{CP} = 2$

g. $m_{CP} = -6$ **h.** $m_{CP} = 0$

2. Find the equation of the tangent at the given point to the given circle:

a. $(4, 3)$; $x^2 + y^2 - 4x - 2y - 3 = 0$ **b.** $(-5, 5)$; $x^2 + y^2 + 6x - 2y - 10 = 0$

c. $(0, -1)$; $x^2 + y^2 + 2x + 10y + 9 = 0$ **d.** $(-5, 1)$; $x^2 + y^2 - 6y - 20 = 0$

e. $(3, -4)$; $x^2 + y^2 - 16x + 35 = 0$ **f.** $(-4, -3)$; $x^2 + y^2 = 25$

g. $(-\frac{1}{2}, 1)$; $x^2 + y^2 - 5x - 6y + \frac{9}{4} = 0$ **h.** $(5, 2)$; $x^2 + y^2 - 4y - 21 = 0$
(Hint: a diagram is essential here.)

3. Find the possible values of k if the given line is a tangent to the circle:

page 41, example 11.5

a. $y = kx$ and $(x - 3)^2 + y^2 = 3$ **b.** $y = x + k$ and $x^2 + y^2 = 5$

c. $y = x - k$ and $(x - 1)^2 + y^2 = 2$

Exercise 11.7 Touching circles

page 41, example 11.6

Determine whether or not the two circles touch:

1. $(x + 2)^2 + y^2 = 4$ and $(x + 1)^2 + (y - 3)^2 = 9$
2. $(x + 1)^2 + (y - 1)^2 = 2$ and $(x - 2)^2 + (y + 2)^2 = 8$
3. $x^2 + y^2 + 4x + 2y = 0$ and $x^2 + y^2 - 12x - 6y = 0$
4. $x^2 + y^2 + 6x - 4y + 3 = 0$ and $x^2 + y^2 - 12x + 2y - 3 = 0$
5. $x^2 + y^2 + 8x - 14y + 52 = 0$ and $x^2 + y^2 - 10x - 2y - 26 = 0$

See these pages in Leckie & Leckie's *Higher Maths Course Notes:*

Exercise 12.1 Interpretation of coordinate diagrams

page 42, example 12.1 **a)**

For these square-based stepped pyramids find the coordinates of the marked points:

1.

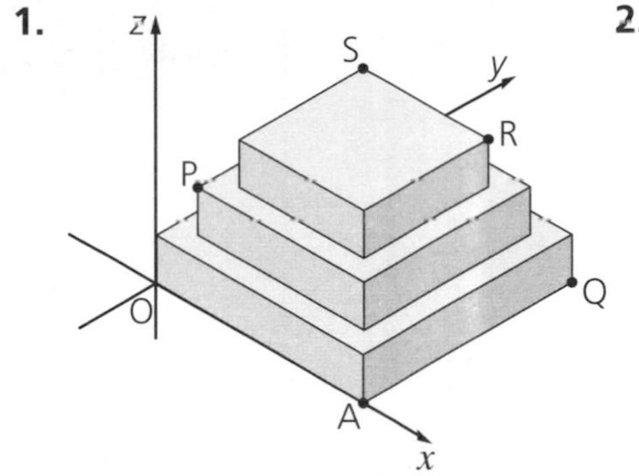

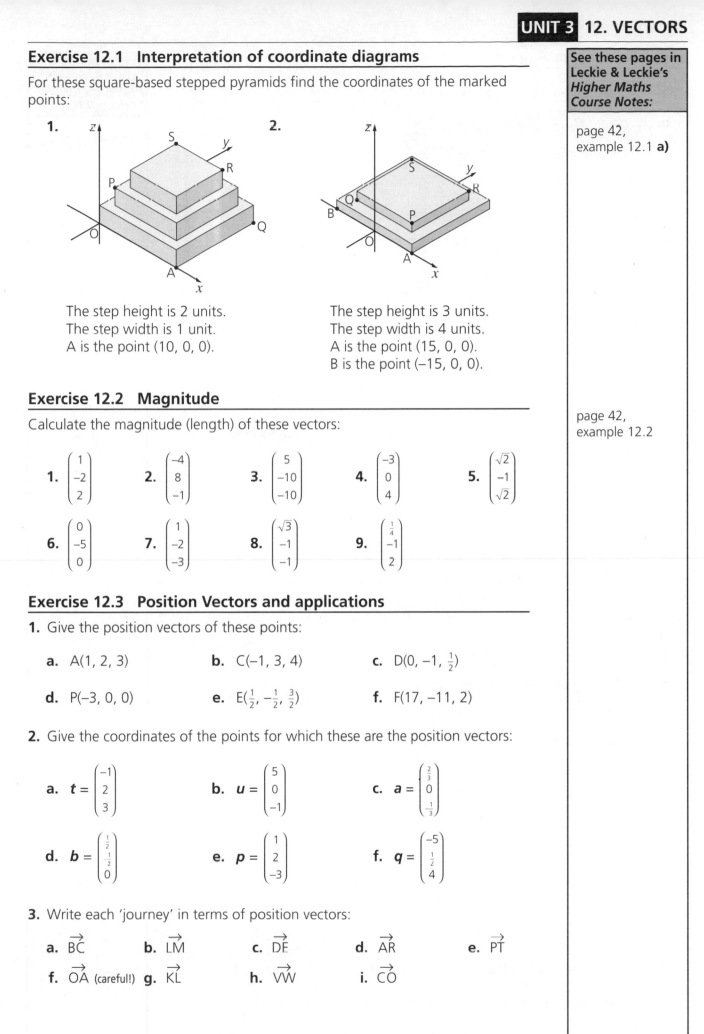

The step height is 2 units.
The step width is 1 unit.
A is the point (10, 0, 0).

2.

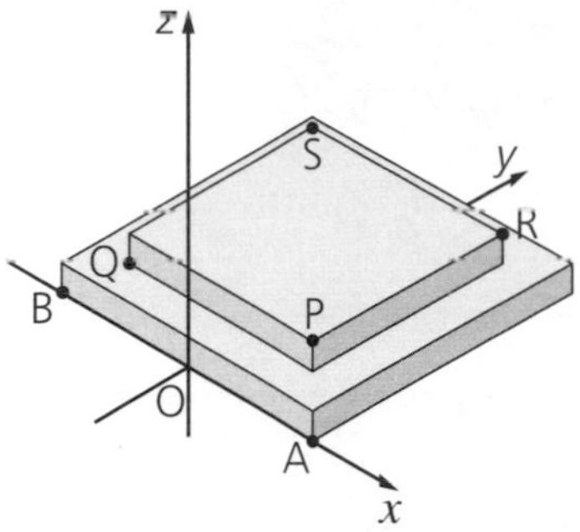

The step height is 3 units.
The step width is 4 units.
A is the point (15, 0, 0).
B is the point (–15, 0, 0).

Exercise 12.2 Magnitude

page 42, example 12.2

Calculate the magnitude (length) of these vectors:

1. $\begin{pmatrix} 1 \\ -2 \\ 2 \end{pmatrix}$ **2.** $\begin{pmatrix} -4 \\ 8 \\ -1 \end{pmatrix}$ **3.** $\begin{pmatrix} 5 \\ -10 \\ -10 \end{pmatrix}$ **4.** $\begin{pmatrix} -3 \\ 0 \\ 4 \end{pmatrix}$ **5.** $\begin{pmatrix} \sqrt{2} \\ -1 \\ \sqrt{2} \end{pmatrix}$

6. $\begin{pmatrix} 0 \\ -5 \\ 0 \end{pmatrix}$ **7.** $\begin{pmatrix} 1 \\ -2 \\ -3 \end{pmatrix}$ **8.** $\begin{pmatrix} \sqrt{3} \\ -1 \\ -1 \end{pmatrix}$ **9.** $\begin{pmatrix} \frac{1}{4} \\ -1 \\ 2 \end{pmatrix}$

Exercise 12.3 Position Vectors and applications

1. Give the position vectors of these points:

a. A(1, 2, 3) **b.** C(–1, 3, 4) **c.** D(0, –1, $\frac{1}{2}$)

d. P(–3, 0, 0) **e.** E($\frac{1}{2}$, $-\frac{1}{2}$, $\frac{3}{2}$) **f.** F(17, –11, 2)

2. Give the coordinates of the points for which these are the position vectors:

a. $\boldsymbol{t} = \begin{pmatrix} -1 \\ 2 \\ 3 \end{pmatrix}$ **b.** $\boldsymbol{u} = \begin{pmatrix} 5 \\ 0 \\ -1 \end{pmatrix}$ **c.** $\boldsymbol{a} = \begin{pmatrix} \frac{2}{3} \\ 0 \\ -\frac{1}{3} \end{pmatrix}$

d. $\boldsymbol{b} = \begin{pmatrix} \frac{1}{2} \\ -\frac{1}{2} \\ 0 \end{pmatrix}$ **e.** $\boldsymbol{p} = \begin{pmatrix} 1 \\ 2 \\ -3 \end{pmatrix}$ **f.** $\boldsymbol{q} = \begin{pmatrix} -5 \\ \frac{1}{2} \\ 4 \end{pmatrix}$

3. Write each 'journey' in terms of position vectors:

a. $\overrightarrow{BC}$ **b.** $\overrightarrow{LM}$ **c.** $\overrightarrow{DE}$ **d.** $\overrightarrow{AR}$ **e.** $\overrightarrow{PT}$

f. $\overrightarrow{OA}$ (careful!) **g.** $\overrightarrow{KL}$ **h.** $\overrightarrow{VW}$ **i.** $\overrightarrow{CO}$

4. Find the components of:

 a. $\overrightarrow{AB}$ where A(–1, 0, 4) and B(6, –1, 3)

 b. $\overrightarrow{RL}$ where R(2, 0, 0) and L(–1, –2, 3)

 c. $\overrightarrow{MN}$ where M(2, 5, –1) and N(–2, –5, 1)

 d. $\overrightarrow{AB}$ where A(0, $\frac{1}{2}$, $\frac{3}{2}$) and B(–1, $-\frac{1}{2}$, $\frac{1}{2}$)

 e. $\overrightarrow{OC}$ where C(–1, 2, 6) (O is the origin)

 f. $\overrightarrow{TS}$ where T(–1, –7, 11) and S(4, 3, 3)

 g. $\overrightarrow{EF}$ where E($\frac{1}{2}$, 2, –1) and F(1, $\frac{3}{2}$, $-\frac{1}{2}$)

 h. $\overrightarrow{KT}$ where K($\sqrt{2}$, 0, $\sqrt{2}$) and T($2\sqrt{2}$, $-\sqrt{2}$, $\sqrt{2}$)

5. A(–1, 2, 1), B(2, 8, 4) and C(0, –3, 3). Use position vectors to find the components of:

 a. $\overrightarrow{AB}$ b. $\overrightarrow{AC}$ c. $\overrightarrow{BC}$ d. $\overrightarrow{CA}$

6. The points P(–1, 0, 2), Q(3, 5, –2), R(–1, 6, –7) and S(–5, 1, –3) form a quadilateral.

 a. Find the components of:

 (i) $\overrightarrow{PQ}$ (ii) $\overrightarrow{SR}$ (iii) $\overrightarrow{QR}$ (iv) $\overrightarrow{PS}$

 b. What sort of quadilateral is PQRS?

Exercise 12.4 Collinearity and Ratio

Show that the three given points are collinear and in each case find the ratio in which the 'middle' point divides the line joining the 'end' points (in the given order).

1. A(2, –1, 4), B(3, 2, 5), C(6, 11, 8)
2. P(1, –1, 3), Q(3, 4, 0), R(7, 14, –6)
3. S(2, –1, –1), T(4, 3, –5), U(5, 5, –7)
4. V(–1, 2, –3), W(2, –4, –3), X(4, –8, –3)
5. D(–1, 3, 5), E(–3, 5, 1), F(–6, 8, –5)
6. J(4, –7, 10), K(0, 1, –2), L(–5, 11, –17)
7. M(25, 25, –10), N(5, 10, –5), P(–3, 4, –3)
8. G($-\frac{3}{2}$, 0, $\frac{7}{2}$), H($\frac{3}{2}$, –1, $\frac{3}{2}$), I(3, $-\frac{3}{2}$, $\frac{1}{2}$)

Exercise 12.5 Find a point dividing a given line

Find the coordinates of:

1. P which divides AB in the ratio 1:2 where A(–1, 0, 4) and B(5, 3, –2)
2. Q which divides CD in the ratio 2:1 where C(1, –3, 4) and D(7, 3, 1)
3. R which divides EF in the ratio 2:3 where E(–5, –2, 1) and F(0, 8, –4)
4. A which divides CD in the ratio 1:5 where C(–2, 1, 3) and D(7, –2, –12)

See these pages in Leckie & Leckie's *Higher Maths Course Notes:*

page 44, example 12.4

page 44, example 12.5

page 45, example 12.7

Exercise 12.6 The angle between two vectors

See these pages in Leckie & Leckie's *Higher Maths Course Notes:*

page 46, example 12.8

1. Use $\cos\theta° = \dfrac{\mathbf{a.b}}{|\mathbf{a}||\mathbf{b}|}$ to find θ:

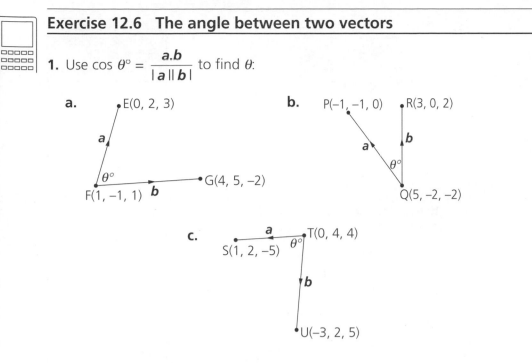

a.

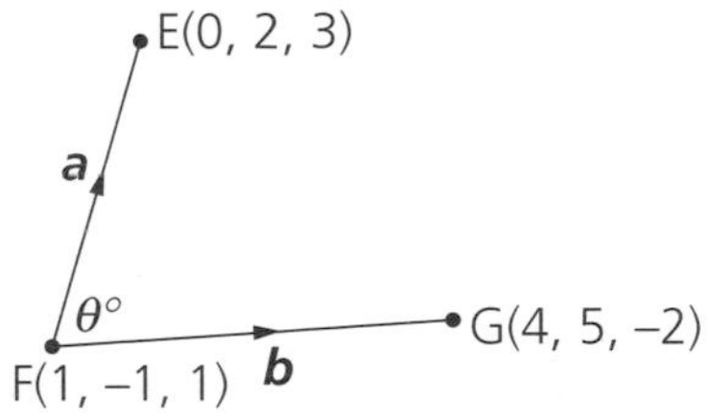

b.

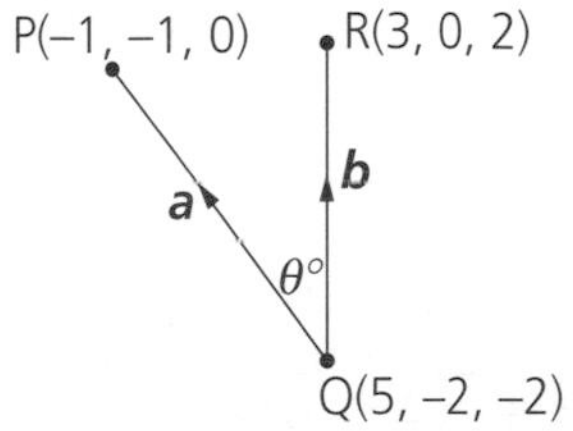

c.

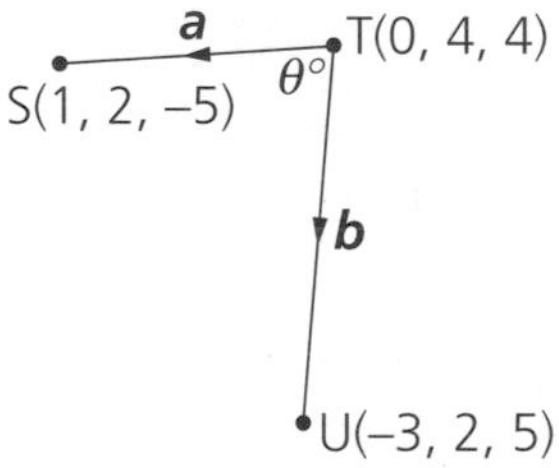

2. Find the size of angle KLM where K(–2, 5, 4), L(–1, 0, –3) and M(2, 2, 8).

3. Find the sizes of the three angles of triangle ABC where A(–1, 3, 5), B(–2, –2, 4) and C(0, 2, 3).

Exercise 12.7 Perpendicular vectors

1. Find the value of k for which the given vectors are perpendicular.

a. $\begin{pmatrix} k \\ 2 \\ 3 \end{pmatrix}$ and $\begin{pmatrix} 1 \\ 1 \\ -1 \end{pmatrix}$ **b.** $\begin{pmatrix} -1 \\ k \\ 3 \end{pmatrix}$ and $\begin{pmatrix} 2 \\ 1 \\ 0 \end{pmatrix}$ **c.** $\begin{pmatrix} -1 \\ 3 \\ k+1 \end{pmatrix}$ and $\begin{pmatrix} 6 \\ -1 \\ 3 \end{pmatrix}$

d. $\begin{pmatrix} -1 \\ -1 \\ -2 \end{pmatrix}$ and $\begin{pmatrix} 2 \\ k-2 \\ -1 \end{pmatrix}$ **e.** $\begin{pmatrix} 0 \\ 3-k \\ 5 \end{pmatrix}$ and $\begin{pmatrix} 2 \\ -1 \\ -2 \end{pmatrix}$ **f.** $\begin{pmatrix} -1 \\ -3 \\ 3 \end{pmatrix}$ and $\begin{pmatrix} 2k-3 \\ 2 \\ -1 \end{pmatrix}$

2. The vectors $\begin{pmatrix} m \\ -2 \\ -1 \end{pmatrix}$ and $\begin{pmatrix} m-1 \\ 1 \\ 4 \end{pmatrix}$ are perpendicular. Find the two possible values for m.

3. Show that triangle ABC is right-angled where A(1, 3, 4), B(3, –1, 0) and C(3, 2, 6).

page 46, example 12.9

4. Show that triangle PQR is right-angled where P(3, 7, –5), Q(5, 9, –4) and R(7, 5, –9) and calculate its area.

Exercise 12.8 Some vector 'algebra'

page 47, example 12.10

1. In each case find the exact value of **a.b** (θ is the angle between **a** and **b**).

a. $|\mathbf{a}| = 2$, $|\mathbf{b}| = 3$ and $\theta° = 60°$ **b.** $|\mathbf{a}| = 2$, $|\mathbf{b}| = 1$ and $\theta° = 30°$

c. $|\mathbf{a}| = 5$, $|\mathbf{b}| = 10$ and $\theta = \frac{\pi}{3}$ **d.** $|\mathbf{a}| = \sqrt{2}$, $|\mathbf{b}| = 1$ and $\theta = \frac{\pi}{4}$

2.

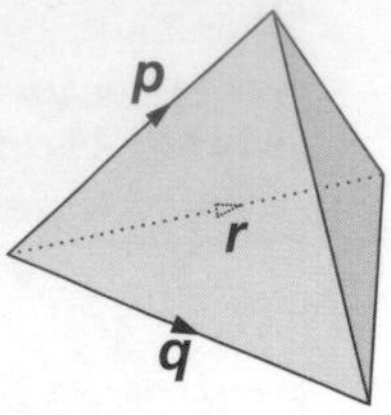

All six edges of this tetrahedron have length 2 units.

Evaluate $\boldsymbol{p}.(\boldsymbol{q} + \boldsymbol{r})$

3.

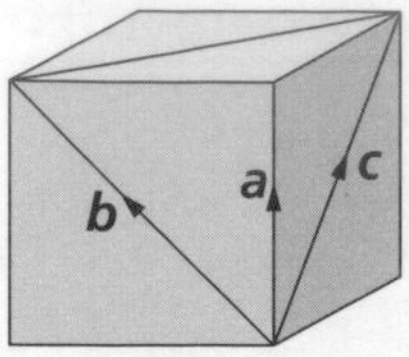

Each edge of this cube has length 1 unit.

a. Find the exact value of $|\boldsymbol{b}|$ and $|\boldsymbol{c}|$

b. Find the exact value of $\boldsymbol{a}.(\boldsymbol{b} + \boldsymbol{c})$

See these pages in Leckie & Leckie's *Higher Maths Course Notes:*

page 47, example 12.10

4.

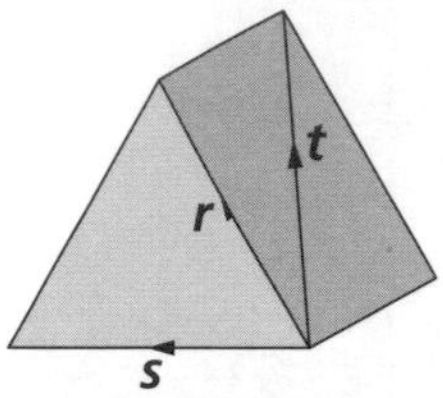

This prism has three square faces and two that are equilateral triangles. All the edges have length 4 units.

Evaluate $\boldsymbol{r}.(\boldsymbol{s} + \boldsymbol{t})$

Exercise 12.9 Basis Vectors

page 47. The first part of example 12.11 should help.

1. Write each of these in column form:

a. $3\boldsymbol{i} - 2\boldsymbol{j} + 5\boldsymbol{k}$ **b.** $4\boldsymbol{i} - \sqrt{2}\boldsymbol{j}$ **c.** $-\boldsymbol{i} - 2\boldsymbol{j} + 8\boldsymbol{k}$ **d.** $-\sqrt{5}\boldsymbol{j} - 2\boldsymbol{k}$

e. $\boldsymbol{i} + \boldsymbol{j} + \boldsymbol{k}$ **f.** $\boldsymbol{i} - \boldsymbol{j} - \boldsymbol{k}$ **g.** $18\boldsymbol{j} - \sqrt{11}\boldsymbol{k}$ **h.** $-\sqrt{2}\boldsymbol{j}$

Page 42, example 12.2 should help.

2. Calculate the magnitude or length of these vectors:

a. $2\boldsymbol{i} - 2\boldsymbol{j} + \boldsymbol{k}$ **b.** $-3\boldsymbol{i} + 6\boldsymbol{j} - 2\boldsymbol{k}$ **c.** $4\boldsymbol{i} - 4\boldsymbol{j} + 7\boldsymbol{k}$ **d.** $4\boldsymbol{i} - 3\boldsymbol{k}$

e. $\boldsymbol{i} - 5\boldsymbol{j} + \sqrt{10}\boldsymbol{k}$ **f.** $\sqrt{5}\boldsymbol{i} + 4\boldsymbol{j} - 2\boldsymbol{k}$ **g.** $2\boldsymbol{j} - \sqrt{5}\boldsymbol{k}$ **h.** $2\sqrt{2}\boldsymbol{i} - \boldsymbol{k}$

i. $\sqrt{5}\boldsymbol{j}$ **j.** $\sqrt{3}\boldsymbol{i} - \boldsymbol{j} - 2\sqrt{3}\boldsymbol{k}$

page 47, example 12.11

3. Find a unit vector parallel to $\boldsymbol{u} + \boldsymbol{v}$ where:

a. $\boldsymbol{u} = 3\boldsymbol{i} - \boldsymbol{j} + 2\boldsymbol{k}$ and $\boldsymbol{v} = -4\boldsymbol{i} - \boldsymbol{j}$

b. $\boldsymbol{u} = \boldsymbol{i} - 5\boldsymbol{j} - 2\boldsymbol{k}$ and $\boldsymbol{v} = \boldsymbol{i} + \boldsymbol{j} + 6\boldsymbol{k}$

c. $\boldsymbol{u} = -2\boldsymbol{i} + 5\boldsymbol{j} - 3\boldsymbol{k}$ and $\boldsymbol{v} = -4\boldsymbol{i} - 2\boldsymbol{j} + \boldsymbol{k}$

See these pages in Leckie & Leckie's *Higher Maths Course Notes:*

Exercise 13.1 The Trig Functions

page 48. The rules are at the top of the page.

1. Differentiate:

a. $\sin x$ **b.** $\cos x$ **c.** $3\sin x$

d. $x^2 - 2\sin x$ **e.** $2x - \cos x$ **f.** $3x^2 - 4\cos x$

g. $\frac{1}{x} - \frac{1}{2}\sin x$ **h.** $\frac{3}{x} - \frac{2}{3}\cos x$ **i.** $1 - 10\cos x$

2. Find:

a. $\int(5x^3 + x + \sin x)\,dx$ **b.** $\int(4x - \cos x)\,dx$

c. $\int(3x^2 - 2x - \sin x)\,dx$ **d.** $\int(6x^3 - 6x^2 + \cos x)\,dx$

e. $\int(10x^4 + 2\cos x)\,dx$ **f.** $\int(5x^2 - x - 3\sin x)\,dx$

g. $\int(8x^3 - 9x^2 - 2\cos x)\,dx$ **h.** $\int(10x + 12x^3 + 4\sin x)\,dx$

Exercise 13.2 Areas under trig graphs

page 48, example 13.1 may help.

1. Find the shaded areas:

a.
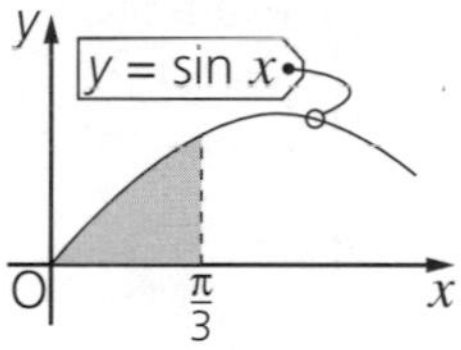

b.
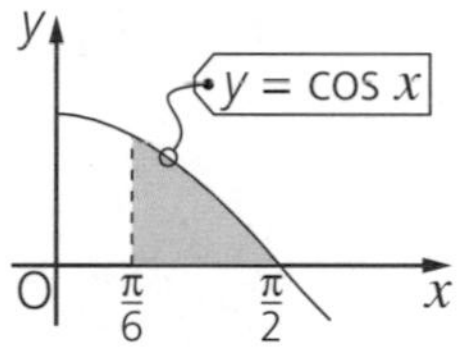

c.
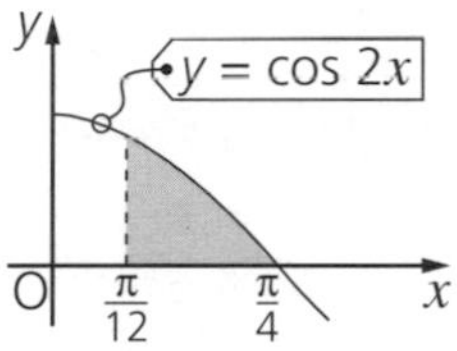

d.
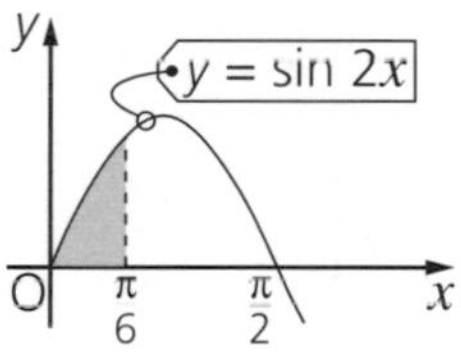

e.
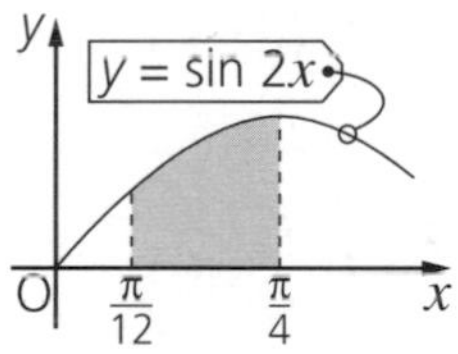

f.
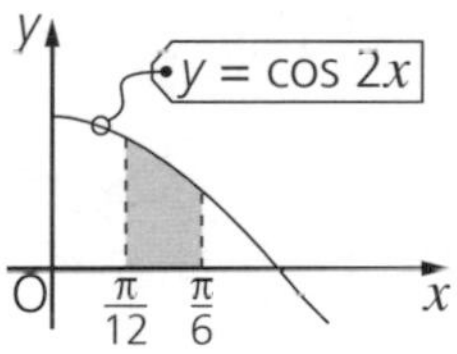

Hint: $\int \sin 2x = \frac{-\cos 2x}{2} + c$ $\int \cos 2x = \frac{\sin 2x}{2} + c$

2. Calculate the area of the shaded shape:
(Careful! The areas are below the x-axis.)

a.
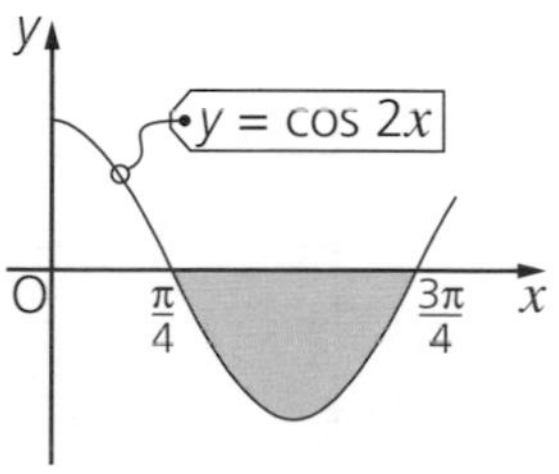

b.
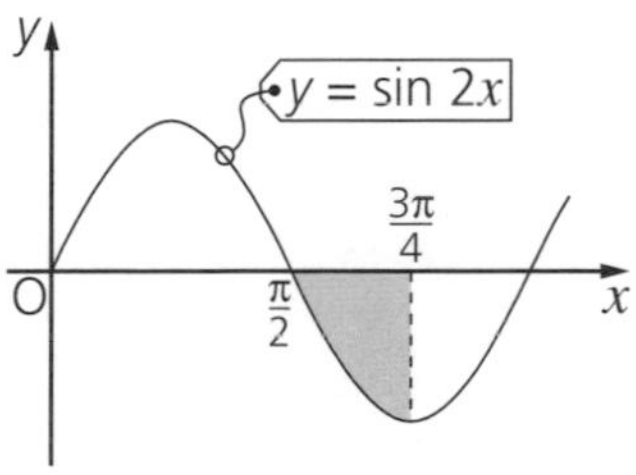

3.
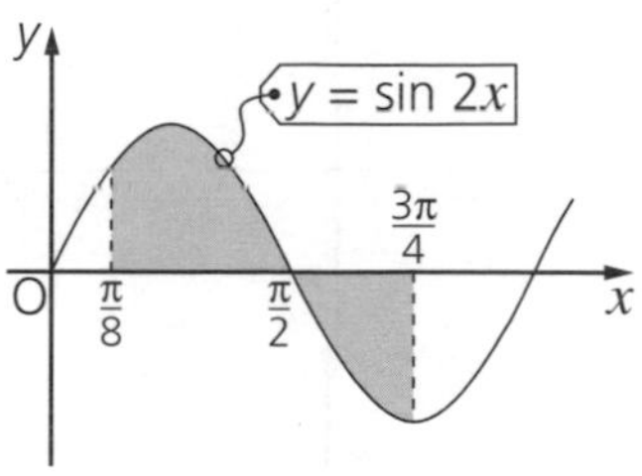

A design for a sand-timer is based on the shaded area in the diagram on the left.

Calculate the area of the shape used for the sand-timer.

Exercise 13.3 The 'Chain Rule'

See these pages in Leckie & Leckie's *Higher Maths Course Notes:*

page 49, example 13.3

Find $\frac{dy}{dx}$, given that:

1. $y = (\sin x + x)^3$ **2.** $y = (x^2 - \cos x)^2$ **3.** $y = \sqrt{x^2 + x}$

4. $y = \sqrt{\sin x - 3}$ **5.** $y = \sqrt{5 - 3\sin x}$ **6.** $y = \cos^2 x$

7. $y = \frac{1}{\sqrt{\cos x}}$ (Hint: Write as $(\cos x)^{-\frac{1}{2}}$) **8.** $y = \frac{1}{\sqrt{\sin x}}$

9. $y = \sqrt{2\cos x - 3}$ **10.** $y = \frac{1}{\cos x}$ (Hint: Write as $(\cos x)^{-1}$)

11. $y = \frac{1}{\cos x + \sin x}$ **12.** $y = \frac{1}{\sin^2 x}$

Exercise 13.4 Special Integrals

page 49, example 13.5

1. Find:

a. $\int (3x-1)^2\,dx$ **b.** $\int (5x+1)^3\,dx$ **c.** $\int (3-2x)^2\,dx$

d. $\int (4+6x)^4\,dx$ **e.** $\int 2(3x+4)^3\,dx$ **f.** $\int 3(5-2x)^2\,dx$

g. $\int (2-x)^4\,dx$ **h.** $\int 6(7-x)^3\,dx$

2. Evaluate:

a. $\int_1^3 x^2\,dx$ **b.** $\int_1^2 (2x-1)^2\,dx$ **c.** $\int_{-1}^1 (3x+1)^3\,dx$

d. $\int_2^4 \left(\frac{1}{2}x-1\right)^3 dx$ **e.** $\int_{-1}^0 (5x-1)^2\,dx$ **f.** $\int_{-\frac{1}{2}}^0 (1-2x)^4\,dx$

g. $\int_{-3}^0 \left(\frac{1}{3}x-2\right)^2 dx$ **h.** $\int_{-4}^0 \left(\frac{1}{4}x+1\right)^7 dx$

Exercise 14.1 Power Statements/Log Statements

See these pages in Leckie & Leckie's *Higher Maths Course Notes:*

page 50, example 14.1

1. Change the following 'power statements' to the corresponding 'log statements'.

a. $92 = 10^x$ **b.** $4 = e^{-y}$ **c.** $e^{2t} = 14{\cdot}1$ **d.** $10^{0{\cdot}5t} = y$

e. $0{\cdot}002 = e^{1.5t}$ **f.** $e^{-5t} = B_3$ **g.** $e^{-2x} = 0{\cdot}5$ **h.** $A_1 = 10^{x+t}$

2. Change these 'log statements' to 'power statements':

a. $\log_2 x = 3$ **b.** $\log_5 10 = x$ **c.** $4 = \log_{10} t$

d. $\log_e A = B$ **e.** $\log_m V_0 = k$ **f.** $\log_b(2A + 1) = T$

page 51, example 14.3

3. Solve for x to 3 significant figures:

a. $\ln x = 2$ **b.** $\log_{10} x = 3{\cdot}1$ **c.** $e^x = 3$ **d.** $10^x = 53$

e. $\log_3 x = 0{\cdot}03$ **f.** $\log_5 x = 0{\cdot}32$ **g.** $e^x = 0{\cdot}03$ **h.** $10^x = 0{\cdot}15$

4. A chemist investigated the cooling rates of various substances under different conditions.

The formula she used was $T_t = T_0 e^{-kt}$ ...where T_0 is the initial temperature (in °C) of the substance and T_t (in °C) is its temperature after t minutes.

The data that she gathered is shown in the table below. Calculate in each case the value of k to 3 significant figures.

	Substance	*Initial Temp (°C)*	*Final Temp (°C)*	*Time elapsed*
a.	Propylamine	40	35	10 min
b.	Butylamine	75	65	$\frac{1}{4}$ hour
c.	Phenylamine	160	130	12 min
d.	Triethylamine	80	79	1 min
e.	Methanoic Acid	75	64	20 min
f.	Ethanoic Acid	100	91	18 min
g.	Propanoic Acid	141	95	$\frac{1}{2}$ hour
h.	Sorbic Acid	228	200	9 min

Hint: Substitute the values into the formula, rearrange to give a 'power statement' then rewrite as a 'log statement'.

See these pages in Leckie & Leckie's *Higher Maths Course Notes:*

5. The amount A grams of a radioactive substance after t units of time is given by $A = A_0e^{-kt}$ where A_0 is the initial amount of the substance and k is a constant.

a. After 8 days, 100 grams of thorium reduces to 74 grams. Use this information to calculate the value of k and hence calculate the half-life of thorium (the length of time, t, after which half the initial amount of the thorium is left).

b. Calculate the half-life of neptunium if it takes 3 hours for 50 grams to reduce to 45·5 grams.

c. Calculate the 'half-life' of each of these isotopes from the given information:

(i) Plutonium has different isotopes. One of them is called plutonium-236. After 3 years 436 grams of this isotope still remained out of 1000 grams.

(ii) For another isotope, plutonium-239, it is estimated that even after 1000 years, 972 grams of an original 1000 grams would still remain.

(iii) Tritium is the only radioactive form of hydrogen. It is used in the luminous dials of watches. 14 grams of this substance decays over the course of 2 years into 12·5 grams.

(iv) A man called Willard Libby developed a method of using the decay of carbon-14, a naturally occurring isotope of carbon, to date wood, seeds and bones. For example, knowing that 15 micrograms of carbon-14 will reduce to 11·8 micrograms over the course of 2000 years allows archaeologists to date samples that they discover.

Exercise 14.2 Laws of Logs

1. Simplify:

page 50, example 14.2

a. $\log_2 100 - 2\log_2 5$ **b.** $\log_{10} 8 + \log_{10} 5 - \log_{10} 4$

c. $\frac{1}{2}\log_6 9 + \log_6 2$ **d.** $\log_4 \sqrt{80} - \log_4 \sqrt{5}$

2. Solve for x:

a. $\log_2(x + 2) + \log_2 4 = 4$ **b.** $\log_5(2x + 3) - \log_5 x = 1$

c. $\log_6(x + 1) + \log_6 x = 1$; $(x > 0)$ **d.** $\log_3(x - 3) + \log_3 x = \log_3 18$; $(x > 0)$

3. Evaluate (to 3 sig figs):

page 51, example 14.5

a. $\log_2 3$ **b.** $\log_5 6$ **c.** $\log_8 40$

d. $\log_4 0{\cdot}2$ **e.** $\log_7(\frac{1}{2})$ **f.** $\log_3 \sqrt{2}$

4. Solve (to 3 sig figs):

page 51, example 14.4

a. $2^x = 1000$ **b.** $3^x = 0{\cdot}1$ **c.** $7^x = \frac{3}{2}$

d. $20^x = 2$ **e.** $5^{-x} = 0{\cdot}01$ **f.** $4^{-0{\cdot}1x} = 0{\cdot}328$

Exercise 14.3 Log graphs

See these pages in Leckie & Leckie's *Higher Maths Course Notes:*

page 51, example 14.6

1. Each diagram shows a sketch of $y = f(x)$, where $f(x) = a\log_2(x - b)$. In each case find the values of a and b.

a.

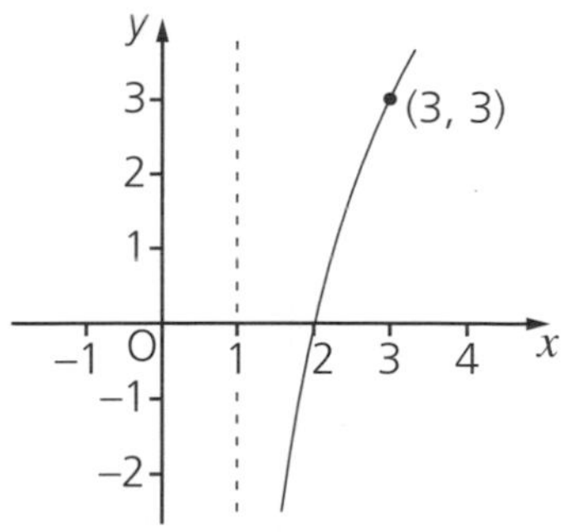

b.

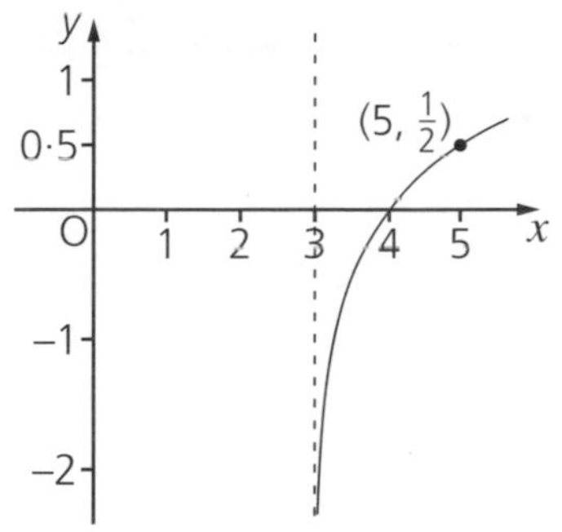

2. Each diagram shows $y = a\log_2(x + b)$. Find the values of a and b.

a.

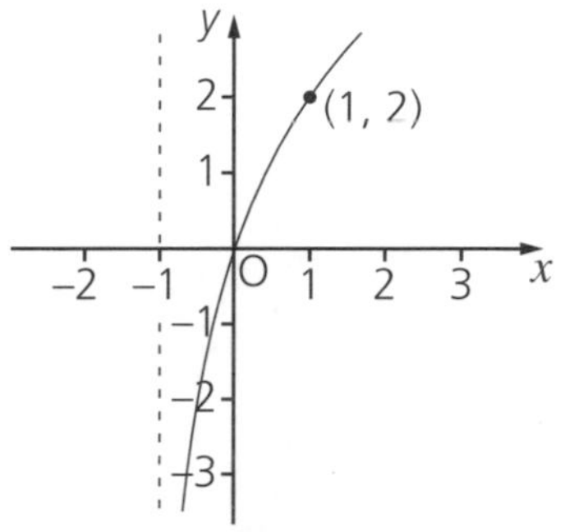

b.

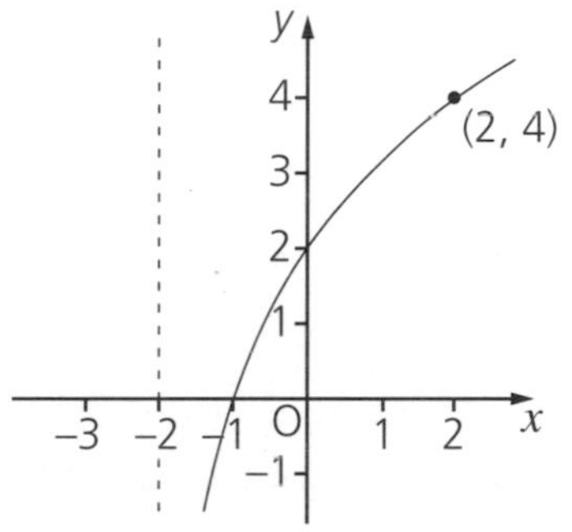

3. Find the formula for each graph (based on the graph of $y = \log_2 x$).

a.

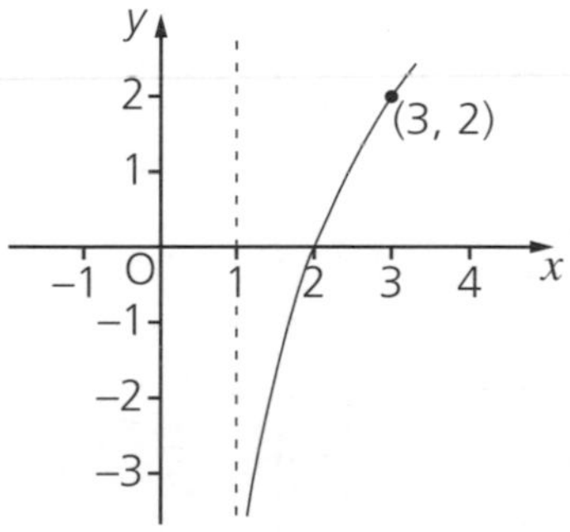

b.

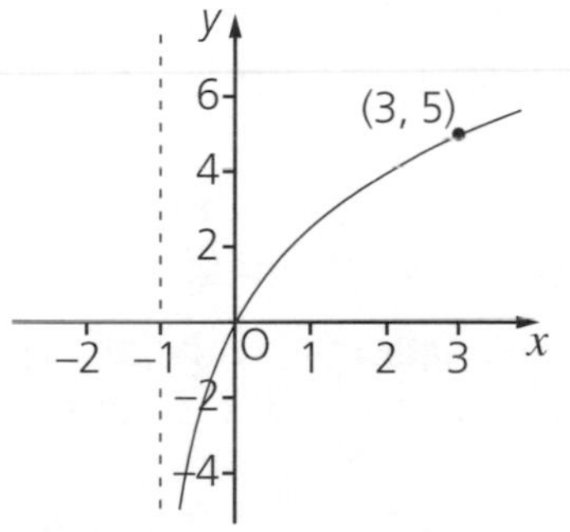

4. The graph of $f(x) = a\log_{10}(x - b)$ crosses the x-axis at (6, 0) and passes through the point (15, 8). Find the values of a and b.

Exercise 14.4 Straight line graphs

page 6, example 1.10

1. Find the equation of the line passing through each pair of points:

a. (2·3, 5·7), (3·3, 7·7)

b. (2, 3·5), (2·5, 3·75)

c. (0·5, 2), (1·25, 0·5)

d. (0, 9·5), (0·2, 9·8)

2. Using a suitable pair of points find the equation of each line in the form $Y = mX + c$

a.

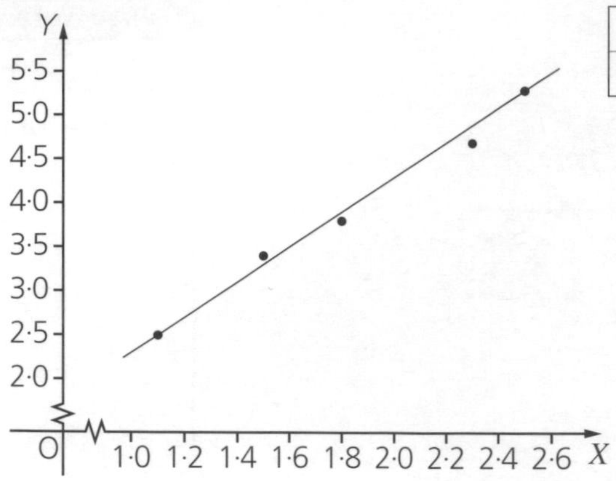

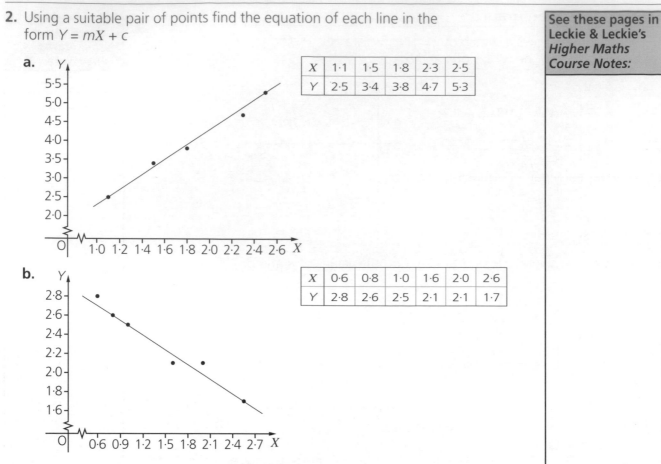

X	1·1	1·5	1·8	2·3	2·5
Y	2·5	3·4	3·8	4·7	5·3

b.

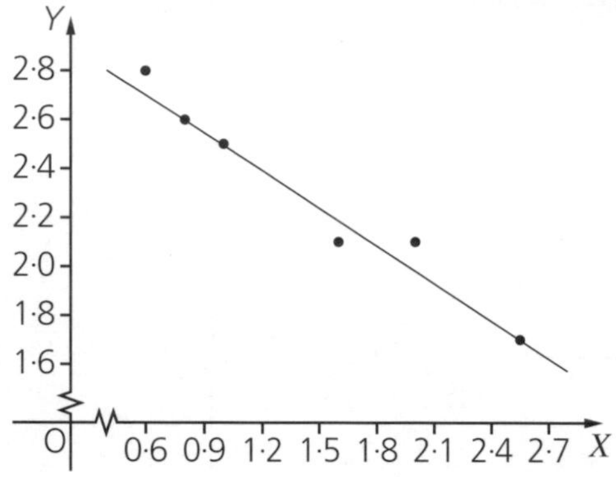

X	0·6	0·8	1·0	1·6	2·0	2·6
Y	2·8	2·6	2·5	2·1	2·1	1·7

3. It is known that x and y are connected by a relationship of the form $y = ax^b$. Find the values of the constants a and b given that:

a. $\log_e y = 2\log_e x + 1{\cdot}5$ **b.** $\log_e y = 3{\cdot}6\log_e x + 0{\cdot}8$ **c.** $\log_e y = 0{\cdot}5\log_e x + 2{\cdot}3$

4. Experimental data is graphed and it is found that the straight line $B = 1{\cdot}2A + 0{\cdot}3$ fits the graph where $A = \log_e x$ and $B = \log_e y$.

It is also thought that x and y are connected by a relationship of the form $y = ax^b$. If this is true then find the values of the constants a and b.

5. The period of oscillation was measured for five different pendulums. It was thought that the length, x metres, of the pendulums and the period, y seconds, were connected by a relationship of the form $y = ax^b$.

After the measurements were taken the following table was constructed and the graph was drawn:

$X (= \log_e x)$	–0·916	–0·511	–0·223	0	0·182
$Y (= \log_e y)$	0·223	0·430	0·561	0·680	0·772

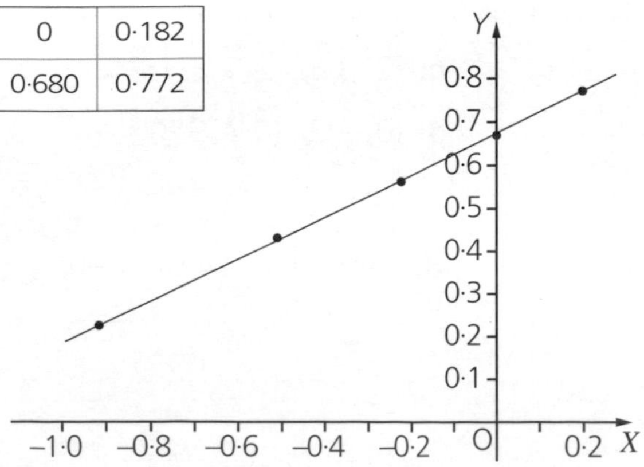

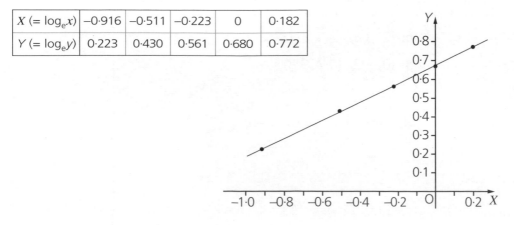

a. Find the equation of the graph in the form $Y = mX + c$.

b. Hence find the values of the constants a and b in the relationship $y = ax^b$.

See these pages in Leckie & Leckie's *Higher Maths Course Notes:*

page 52.
The notes on this page and example 14.8 should help.

Exercise 15.1 Simultaneous Equations

See these pages in Leckie & Leckie's *Higher Maths Course Notes:*

page 53. The notes and example 15.1 should help.

1. Find x for each pair of equations, where $0 \le x \le 360$ and $k > 0$:

a. $k\sin x° = 1$, $k\cos x° = 2$ **b.** $k\sin x° = 3$, $k\cos x° = 2$

c. $k\sin x° = \sqrt{3}$, $k\cos x° = 1$ **d.** $k\sin x° = 3$, $k\cos x° = 3$

2. Find k for each pair of equations ($k > 0$):

a. $k\sin x° = 2$, $k\cos x° = 1$ **b.** $k\sin x° = 5$, $k\cos x° = 3$

c. $k\sin x° = \sqrt{3}$, $k\cos x° = 2$ **d.** $k\sin x° = 1$, $k\cos x° = \sqrt{2}$

3. Solve these simultaneous equations where $k > 0$ and $0 \le \alpha \le 360$:

a. $k\sin \alpha° = 4$, $k\cos \alpha° = 3$ **b.** $k\sin \alpha° = \sqrt{7}$, $k\cos \alpha° = 1$

c. $k\sin \alpha° = 5$, $k\cos \alpha° = 5$ **d.** $k\sin \alpha° = 8$, $k\cos \alpha° = 3$

e. $k\sin \alpha° = \sqrt{3}$, $k\cos \alpha° = \sqrt{5}$ **f.** $k\sin \alpha° = \sqrt{10}$, $k\cos \alpha° = \sqrt{5}$

Exercise 15.2 Linear combinations of Sine and Cosine

page 53, example 15.1 and page 54, example 15.2

In each case express $f(x)$ in the given form with $k > 0$ and $0 \le \alpha < 360$.

1. $f(x) = 3\cos x° + 4\sin x°$ in the form $k\cos (x - \alpha)°$

[use $\cos (x - \alpha)° = \cos x° \cos \alpha° + \sin x° \sin \alpha°$]

2. $f(x) = 5\sin x° + 12\cos x°$ in the form $k\sin (x + \alpha)°$

[use $\sin (x + \alpha)° = \sin x° \cos \alpha° + \cos x° \sin \alpha°$]

3. $f(x) = \sin x° - 2\cos x°$ in the form $k\sin (x - \alpha)°$

4. $f(x) = 2\cos x° - 5\sin x°$ in the form $k\cos (x + \alpha)°$

5. $f(x) = \sqrt{3}\cos x° + \sin x°$ in the form $k\cos (x - \alpha)°$

6. $f(x) = \sqrt{2}\sin x° - \sqrt{2}\cos x°$ in the form $k\sin (x - \alpha)°$

Exercise 15.3 Solving equations

page 54, example 15.3

1. Solve algebraically for $0 \le x < 360$:

a. $\sqrt{7}\cos (x - 35)° = 2$ **b.** $3\sin (x - 15{\cdot}3)° = 1$

c. $5\cos (x + 9{\cdot}2)° = -3$ **d.** $\sqrt{3}\sin (x + 24{\cdot}6)° = -0{\cdot}5$

2. $f(x) = 3\cos x° + \sin x°$

a. Express $f(x)$ in the form $k\cos (x - \alpha)°$ where $k > 0$ and $0 \le \alpha < 360$.

b. Hence solve algebraically $f(x) = -0{\cdot}5$ for $0 \le x < 360$.

See these pages in Leckie & Leckie's *Higher Maths Course Notes:*

3. $g(x) = \sqrt{3}\sin x° - \cos x°$

   a. Express $g(x)$ in the form $k\sin(x - \alpha)°$ where $k > 0$ and $0 \le \alpha < 360$.

   b. Hence solve algebraically $g(x) = 0{\cdot}8$ for $0 \le x < 360$.

4. Solve $4\sin x° - 3\cos x° = 2{\cdot}3$ for $0 \le x \le 360$.

Exercise 15.4 Maximum and Minimum Values

page 55, example 15.4

1. In each case give the maximum and minimum value of f and the corresponding values of x, where $0 \le x \le 360$.

   a. $f(x) = 2\sin(x + 20)°$
   b. $f(x) = 3\cos(x - 30)°$
   c. $f(x) = \sqrt{2}\cos(x + 10)°$
   d. $f(x) = 2\sqrt{3}\sin(x + 100)°$
   e. $f(x) = 10\sin(x - 100)°$
   f. $f(x) = 2{\cdot}6\cos(x + 120)°$

2. Find the maximum and minimum values of these expressions and the corresponding values of θ for $0 \le \theta \le 360$.

   a. $7\sin\theta° + 24\cos\theta°$
   b. $12\cos\theta° - 5\sin\theta°$
   c. $3\sin\theta° - 4\cos\theta°$
   d. $5\sin\theta° + 12\cos\theta°$
   e. $\cos\theta° - 3\sin\theta°$
   f. $3\cos\theta° + 2\sin\theta°$

EXAM A PAPER 1

Time 1 hr 15 min **No calculators**

All questions should be attempted.

1. A(3, –1), B(–1, 3) and C(–2, 0) are the vertices of triangle ABC as shown in the diagram. M is the midpoint of AB. Find the equation of the line through M perpendicular to BC.

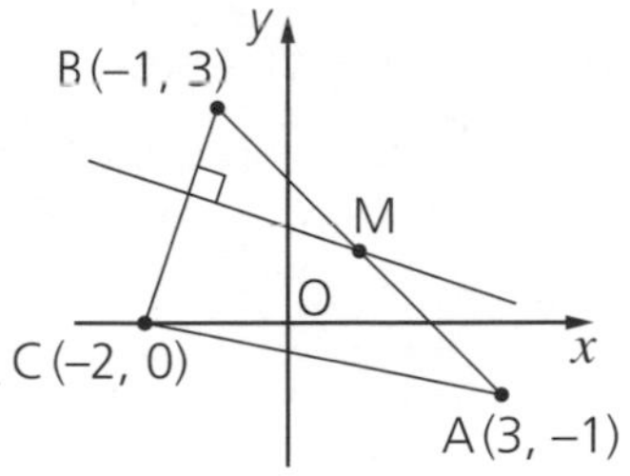

(4)

2. A sequence is defined by the recurrence relation $u_{n+1} = au_n + b$ with first term $u_1 = 5$.

a. State the condition for this sequence to have a limit as n tends to infinity. **(1)**

b. If $u_2 = 8$ and $u_3 = 9{\cdot}5$ calculate the values of a and b. **(3)**

c. Find the exact value of the limit of this sequence as n tends to infinity. **(2)**

3. a. Show that $(x - 2)$ is a factor of $f(x) = 4x^3 - 12x^2 + 5x + 6$ and find the other factors. **(3)**

b. State the coordinates of the points where the graph $y = f(x)$ meets the x-axis. **(1)**

4. If x is an acute angle such that $\sin x = \frac{2}{3}$, show that the exact value of $\cos(x + \frac{\pi}{6})$ is $\frac{\sqrt{15} - 2}{6}$. **(3)**

5. The solid in the diagram is a cuboctahedron and is constructed by slicing the corners off a cube. Vertices A, B, C and D have coordinates as shown.

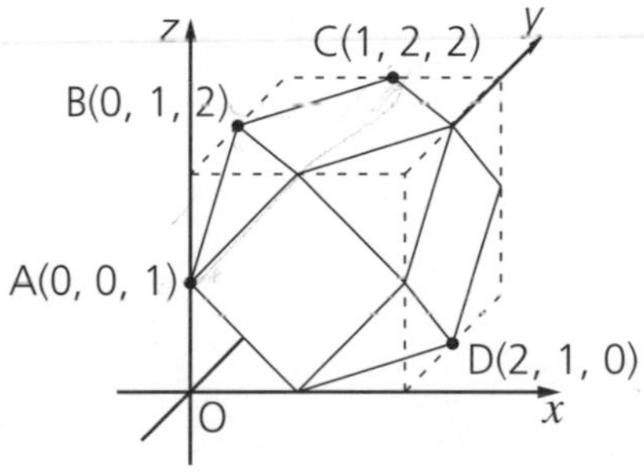

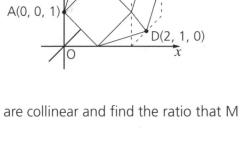

a. Show that the cosine of angle ABC is $-\frac{1}{2}$. **(5)**

b. M is the midpoint of AC. Show that B, M and D are collinear and find the ratio that M divides BD.

(5)

6. The diagram shows the design stage for a tambourine with four jingles. The line of centres of the tambourine (large circle) and the upper and lower jingles (small circles) is parallel to the y-axis. The centres of all four jingles lie on the circumference of the tambourine. The tambourine touches the x-axis and two of the jingles touch the y-axis as shown.

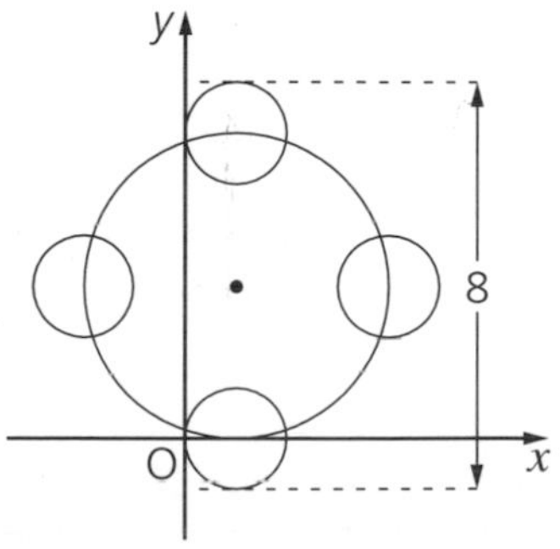

If the equation of the tambourine (large circle) is $x^2 + y^2 - 2x - 6y + 1 = 0$ find the equation of the upper jingle (small circle). **(5)**

7. Find the value of $\int_{-2}^{-1} \frac{6x^3 - x}{3x^3}\, dx$. **(5)**

8. Sketch the graph of $y = 3\sin(x + 30)^\circ$ for $0 \leq x \leq 360$. **(4)**

9. Find $\frac{dy}{dx}$ given that $y = \frac{1}{\sin^2 x}$. **(3)**

10. Part of the graph of $y = 2 - \log_3(x + 1)$ is shown. It crosses the x-axis at A, the y-axis at B and the line $y = 3$ at C.

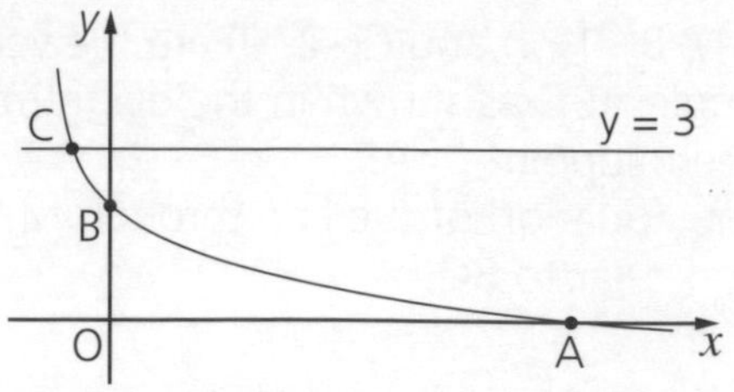

Find:

a. The x-coordinate of point A **(2)**

b. The y-coordinate of point B **(1)**

c. The coordinates of point C. **(3)**

TOTAL: 50

EXAM A PAPER 2

Time 1 hr 45 min **Calculators allowed**

All questions should be attempted.

1. PQRS is a rhombus. P, Q and R have coordinates P(–2, –1), Q(–1, 4) and R(4, 5). Find the equation of SR. **(3)**

2. Two different types of water-purifying machines are in use. Type A removes 35% of pollutants each day and is used in a tank which receives 15 litres of new pollutant at the end of each day. Type B daily removes 60% of pollutants but is operating in a tank where 25 litres of new pollutant are dumped after each day's operation. In the long run which tank contains less pollutant? **(5)**

3. **a.** Show that the function $f(x) = 3x^2 - 6x + 2$ can be written in the form $a(x + b)^2 + c$ where a, b and c are constants. **(3)**

b. Hence, or otherwise, find the coordinates of the minimum turning point of the graph $y = f(x)$. **(1)**

4. The diagram shows the cross-section of a wall of a hillside irrigation trench which has been modelled by the curve $y = x^3 - 2x + 1$.

The surface of the hillside has been modelled by QP, the tangent to the curve at P(1, 0).

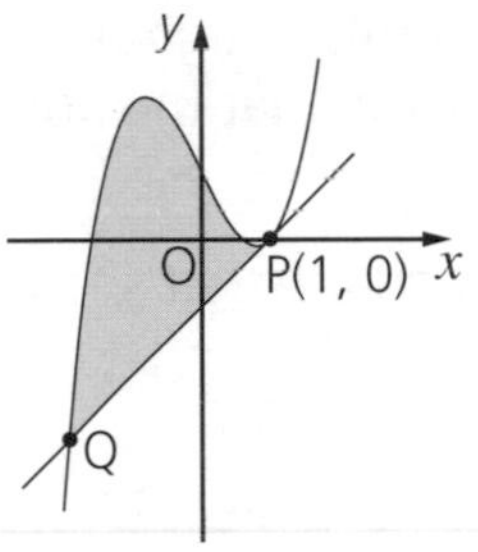

a. Find the equation of the tangent QP. **(3)**

b. Find the coordinates of Q. **(4)**

c. Calculate the area of the shaded cross-section of the wall of the trench. **(3)**

5. The diagram shows two identically sized circles that have line AB as a common tangent with T as the point of contact. The equation of AB is $x = -2$.

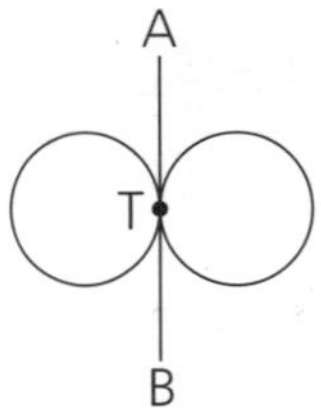

a. One of the circles has equation $x^2 + y^2 - 2x + 2y - 7 = 0$. Find the equation of the other circle. **(3)**

b. A third circle is to be added to the figure in such a way that the other two circles lie inside it. The third circle has equation $x^2 + y^2 + 4x + 2y + c = 0$. Find the range of possible values of c. **(3)**

6. PQRS is a tetrahedron with four congruent faces that are equilateral triangles. The length of PQ is 4 units.

$\overrightarrow{PQ} = \boldsymbol{a}$, $\overrightarrow{PR} = \boldsymbol{b}$ and $\overrightarrow{PS} = \boldsymbol{c}$.

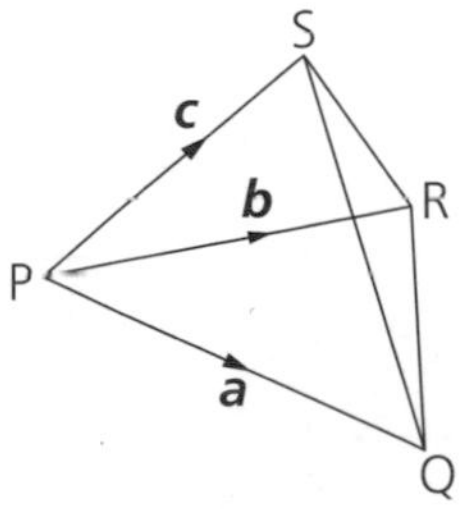

a. Evaluate $\boldsymbol{a}.(\boldsymbol{b} + \boldsymbol{c})$. **(3)**

b. (i) Express $\overrightarrow{SR}$ in terms of $\boldsymbol{b}$ and $\boldsymbol{c}$. **(1)**

(ii) Hence show that $\overrightarrow{SR}$ is perpendicular to $\overrightarrow{PQ}$. **(3)**

7. $f(x) = \cos x° - 5\sin x°$

   a. Express $f(x)$ in the form $k\cos(x + \alpha)°$ where $k > 0$ and $0 \le \alpha \le 360$. **(4)**

   b. Hence solve $f(x) = 1$ for $0 \le x < 360$. **(3)**

   c. The graph $y = f(x)$ cuts the x-axis at the point $(a, 0)$ where $180 < a < 270$. Find the value of a. **(2)**

8. **a.** Show that $\cos^2 x° - \cos 2x° = 1 - \cos^2 x°$. **(1)**

   b. Hence solve the equation $3\cos^2 x° - 3\cos 2x° = 8\cos x°$ in the interval $0 \le x < 90$. **(4)**

9. The roots of the equation $(kx + 2)(x + 3) = 8$ are equal. Find the values of k. **(5)**

10. A window design is in the shape of a rectangular pane of clear glass with two semi-circular panes of frosted glass as shown in the diagram. The rectangular pane measures $2x$ metres by w metres.

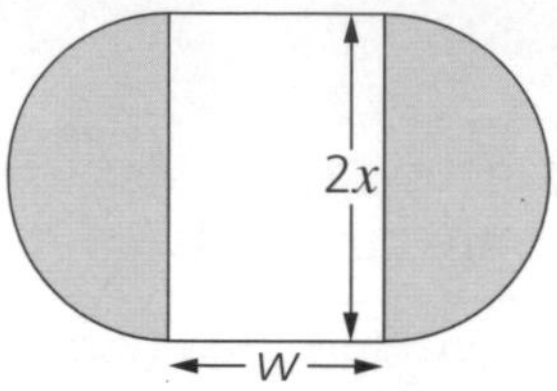

   a. If the perimeter of the window is 8 metres express w in terms of x. **(2)**

   b. Clear glass lets in 3 units of light per square metre and frosted glass lets in 2 units of light per square metre. Show that the number of units of light, L, let in by the window is given by $L = 24x - 4\pi x^2$. **(3)**

   c. Find the values of x and w that should be used to allow the window to let in the maximum amount of light. **(4)**

11. The average distance, x units (taking $x = 1$ for the Earth), of a planet from the sun and the time, y years, of one revolution round the sun are thought to be connected by a relationship of the form $y = ax^b$. Using data for the five planets closest to the sun in our own solar system the following table was constructed and a graph drawn:

	Mercury	Venus	Earth	Mars	Jupiter
$X (= \log_e x)$	−0·949	−0·324	0	0·421	1·649
$Y (= \log_e y)$	−1·423	−0·485	0	0·632	2·473

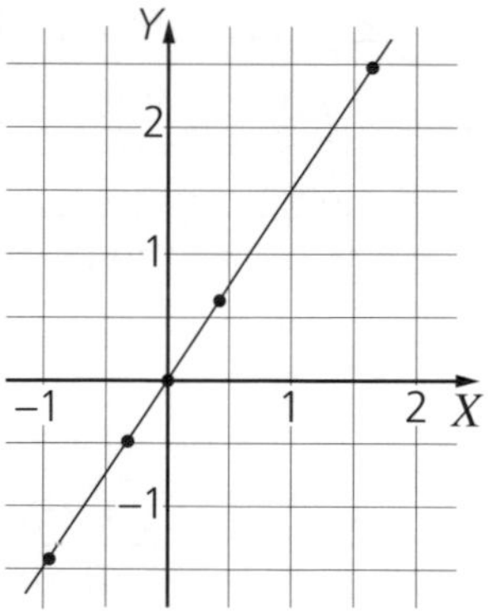

   a. Find the equation of the best-fitting line (shown in the diagram) in the form $Y = mX + c$. **(1)**

   b. Hence find good estimates for the values of the constants a and b in the relationship $y = ax^b$. **(3)**

   c. It is known that Uranus takes very close to 84 years to complete one revolution round the sun. Use the relationship you discovered to estimate the distance of Uranus from the sun. **(3)**

TOTAL: 70

EXAM B PAPER 1

Time 1 hr 15 min **No calculators**

All questions should be attempted.

1. A(1, 2), B(−3, −1) and C(4, −2) are the vertices of triangle ABC as shown in the diagram.

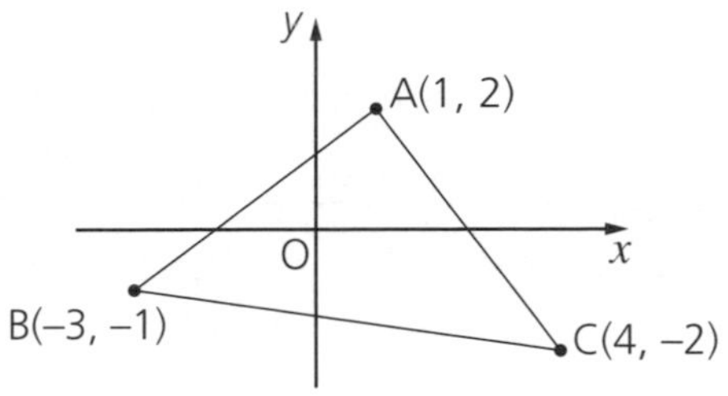

a. Show that triangle ABC is isosceles. **(3)**

b. Side AB makes an angle θ with the positive direction of the x-axis. Find the exact value of tan θ. **(2)**

2. The functions f and g are defined on a suitable domain by $f(x) = 2x^2$ and $g(x) = 4 - x^2$.

a. Find an expression for $g(f(x))$. **(2)**

b. Factorise $g(f(x))$ fully. **(2)**

3. Differentiate $\frac{2x+6}{\sqrt{x}}$ with respect to x. **(4)**

4. A sequence is defined by the recurrence relation $u_{n+1} = \frac{7}{10}u_n + 2$ with $u_0 = 5$.

a. Explain why this sequence has a limit as $n \to \infty$. **(1)**

b. Find the exact value of this limit. **(2)**

c. The multiplier $\frac{7}{10}$ is altered so that the limit of the sequence is increased to the nearest positive integer. Calculate the exact value of this new multiplier. **(3)**

5. The diagram shows part of the graph $y = \sin x$. The points A and B on the graph have coordinates A$(\frac{\pi}{6}, a)$ and B$(\frac{\pi}{2}, b)$.

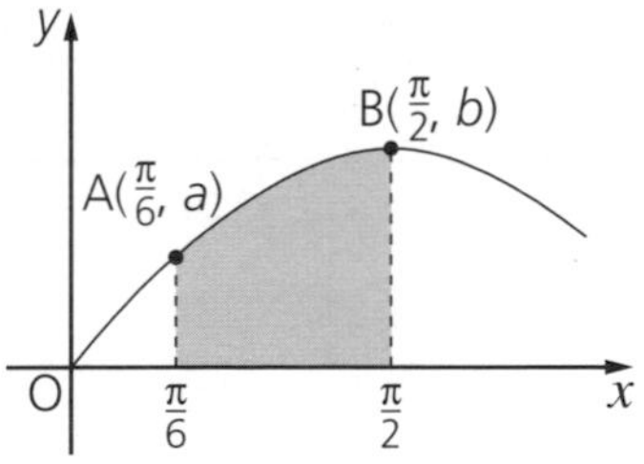

a. Write down the values of a and b. **(1)**

b. Find the exact value of the area of the shaded region. **(4)**

6. The diagram shows a sketch of part of a cubic graph $y = f(x)$ with stationary points $(0, a)$ and (b, c).

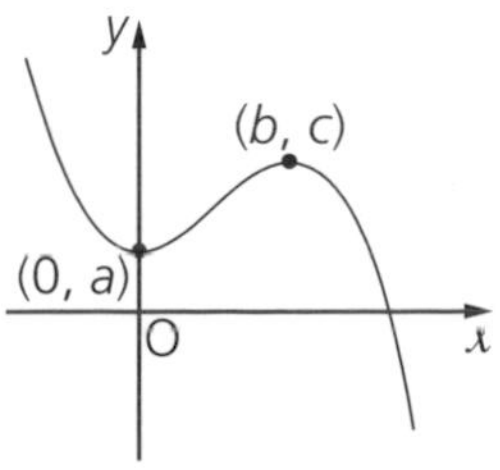

a. Sketch the graph of $y = f(x - 1)$. **(2)**

b. On a separate diagram sketch the graph of $y = f'(x)$. **(2)**

7. Part of the graphs of $y = 2\sqrt{x+1}$ and $2y - 3x = 6$ are shown in the diagram. A tangent to the curve is drawn parallel to the given straight line.

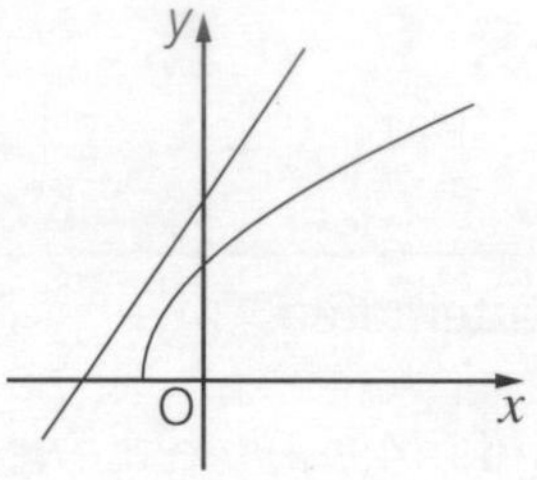

Find the x-coordinate of the point of contact of this tangent to the curve. **(4)**

8. A parabolic curve with equation $y = kx(3 - x)$, where k is a positive integer, has the line with equation $y = x + 1$ as a tangent.

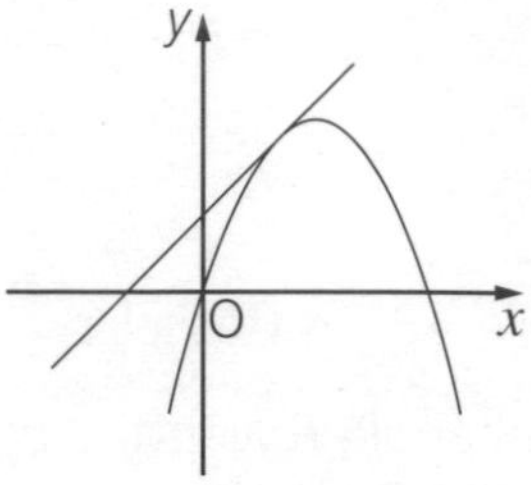

Determine the value of k. **(5)**

9. **a.** Show that $(\sin A + \cos B)^2 + (\cos A + \sin B)^2 = 2 + 2\sin (A + B)$ **(3)**

b. Hence, if $(\sin A + \cos B)^2 + (\cos A + \sin B)^2 = 3$, find two possible values for angle $(A + B)$ between 0 and 2π. **(3)**

10. The position vectors of the points P and Q are $\boldsymbol{p} = 3\boldsymbol{i} + 4\boldsymbol{j}$ and $\boldsymbol{q} = -3\boldsymbol{i} - 4\boldsymbol{j} + 5\boldsymbol{k}$ respectively. Calculate the size of angle POQ, where O is the origin. **(4)**

11. The line $y = x$ is a tangent to the circle with centre $(0, a)$ and radius 2 units as shown in the diagram.

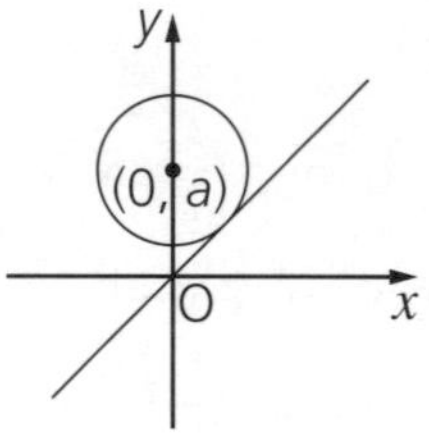

Find the exact value of a and hence find the equation of the circle. **(3)**

TOTAL: 50

EXAM B PAPER 2

Time 1 hr 45 min **Calculators allowed**

All questions should be attempted.

1. The vectors $\mathbf{a} = p\mathbf{i} - \mathbf{k}$ and $\mathbf{b} = 2\mathbf{i} + \mathbf{j} + \mathbf{k}$ are perpendicular. Find:

   a. The value of p **(2)**

   b. $|\mathbf{a}|$ and $|2\mathbf{a} - \mathbf{b}|$ **(2)**

   c. $\mathbf{a}.(2\mathbf{a} - \mathbf{b})$ **(1)**

   d. The angle between $\mathbf{a}$ and $2\mathbf{a} - \mathbf{b}$. **(2)**

2. A preliminary partial sketch of the curve with equation $y = 3 + 2x^2 - x^4$ is shown in the diagram.

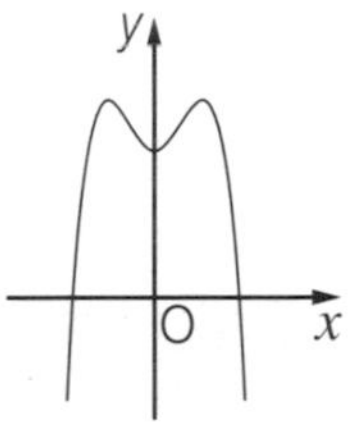

   a. Find the coordinates of the stationary points on the curve. **(6)**

   b. Confirm the information in the sketch by determining the nature of the stationary points. **(3)**

   c. Find the minimum value of y for $0 \leq x \leq 1{\cdot}5$. **(2)**

3. The graph with equation $y = a(x - b)^2 + c$ has a minimum turning point (6, 8).

   a. State the values of b and c. **(2)**

   b. If the graph has gradient -1 at the point with x-coordinate 5 calculate the value of a. **(2)**

4. The diagram shows the circle with equation $x^2 + y^2 + 4x + 2y - 15 = 0$. A line with gradient 2 passes through C, the centre of the circle, and intersects the circle at points A and B as shown in the diagram.

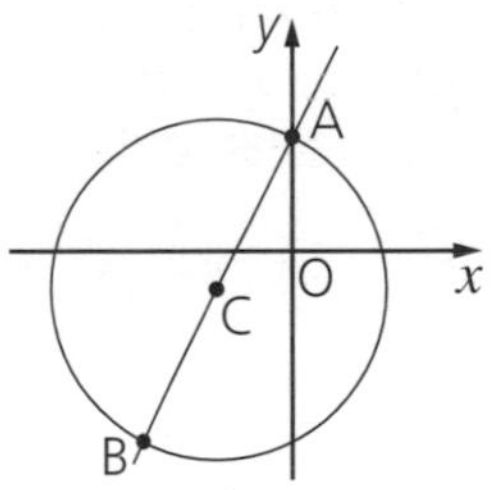

   a. Find the equation of the line AB and hence show that A lies on the x-axis. **(5)**

   b. Find the equation of the tangent to the circle at the point B. **(3)**

5. A metal component is in the form of a prism with cross-sectional area bounded by the curves with equations $y = 4\sqrt{x}$ and $y = 5 - x^2$ as shown in the diagram (all measurements are in centimetres). 30,000 of these components are to be produced.

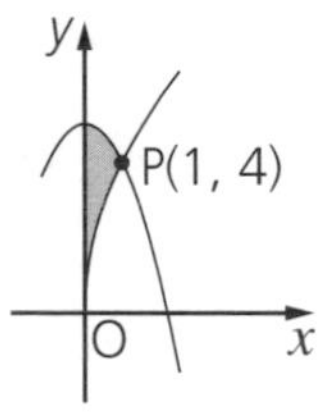

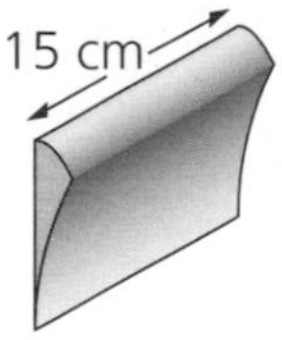

   What total volume of metal will be required if 11% of this total is added to allow for wastage in the casting process? **(6)**

6. The function f is defined by $f(\theta) = 3\cos\theta° - \sin\theta°$.

   a. Show that $f(\theta)$ can be expressed in the form $f(\theta) = k\cos(\theta + \alpha)°$ where $k > 0$ and $0 \leq \alpha \leq 360$ and determine the values of k and α. **(4)**

   b. Hence find the maximum and minimum values of $f(\theta)$ and the corresponding values of θ, where θ lies in the interval $0 \leq \theta < 360$. **(4)**

   c. Write down the minimum value of $\sqrt{10}(3\cos\theta° - \sin\theta°) + 10$. **(1)**

7. An allometric law connecting two variables x and y is of the form $y = ax^b$ where a and b are constants.

   a. Show that if x and y obey an allometric law then there is a linear relationship between $\log_e y$ and $\log_e x$. **(2)**

   b. It is known that an allometric law exists between face length (x mm) and skull length (y mm) for a particular species of baboon:

x	31·9	138·7
y	78·5	122·0

   Use this data to find the law (i.e. determine a and b). **(5)**

8. The function $f(x) = x^4 + 4x^3 + 5x^2 + 14x + 24$

$$= (x + a)(x + b)(x^2 - x + 4)$$

   a. Find the values of a and b. **(2)**

   b. Hence show that the equation $f(x) = 0$ has only two real solutions. **(2)**

9. A cuboid is to be cut from a long wedge of wood as shown in the diagram. The wedge is in the shape of a prism with a right-triangular end with base 20 cm and height 10 cm. When cut, the cuboid has to have dimensions x cm × h cm × $6x$ cm.

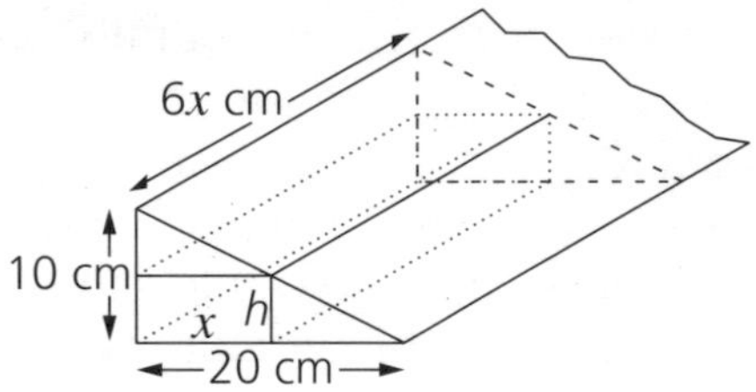

   a. 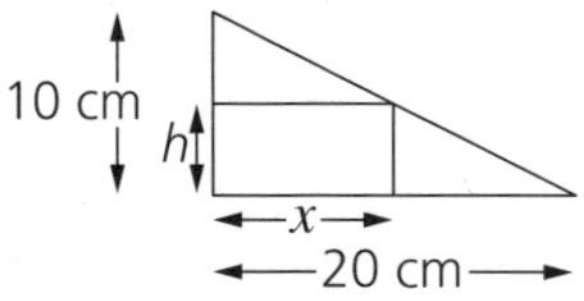

   Show that $h = 10 - \frac{1}{2}x$ **(3)**

   b. Show that the volume, V cm³, of the cuboid is given by $V(x) = 60x^2 - 3x^3$ **(1)**

   c. Hence find the dimensions of the cuboid with the greatest volume that can be cut from the wedge. **(5)**

10. Given that $5 \times 3^{\alpha} = 2$ where $\alpha = \cos^2 x - \sin^2 x$, calculate the smallest possible positive value of x. **(5)**

TOTAL: 70